INDIAN FICTION IN ENGLISH

An Annotated Bibliography

INDIAN FICTION IN ENGLISH

An Annotated Bibliography

DOROTHY M. SPENCER

South Asia Regional Studies
University of Pennsylvania

Philadelphia
UNIVERSITY OF PENNSYLVANIA PRESS

© 1960 by the Trustees of the University of Pennsylvania

Published in Great Britain, India and Pakistan
by the Oxford University Press
London, Bombay and Karachi

Library of Congress Catalogue Card Number: 59–13439

Printed in Great Britain
by W. & J. Mackay & Co Ltd, Chatham

CONTENTS

INDIAN FICTION IN ENGLISH

An Annotated Bibliography

Introductory Essay on
Indian Society, Culture and Fiction

THE NOVEL as a literary form in India is a product of the British impact. *Ālāler Gharer Dulāl*,[1] generally considered the first Indian novel, was published in 1858. Its author, Piari Chand Mitra, is indebted to certain early nineteenth century forerunners,[2] who, like himself, wrote in Bengali, but his work, while it reflects from various angles the results of British influence upon his society and culture, appears to owe relatively little to Bengali literature of the pre-British period. Bengalis led the way, but writers in other vernaculars were not slow in adopting the new forms of fiction, the novel and the short story.

Kroeber, in his article on *The Novel in Asia and Europe*, commented upon the absence of the novel in India and suggested that while its development "may have been inhibited partly by the epic . . . a larger factor is likely to have been the Hindu penchant for extravagant exaggeration, which alone would be fatal to the novel as here defined."[3] Still more important, I believe, was a lack of interest in the events of ordinary life as lived by man on this earth, combined with a lack of interest in the observable differences in the personal characters of particular individuals. S. K. De, examining the "obstacles, both internal and external, which stood effectively in the way" of the development of modern drama from the Bengali *yātrā* (religious play) writes: "The external world had

9

never possessed any inherent interest to the naturally stoical and idealistic Hindu . . . A majestic common sense, and rich feeling for the concrete facts and forces of human nature and human life, a sense of enjoyment of the good things of earth, a passion of energy and action are traits which foster material civilization but which are antagonistic to Hindu ideas of placid contentment, to the insensibility, amazement and ecstasy of religious devotion, to the wistfulness and pathos of spiritual desire."[4] It is interesting to note the reactions, as recorded by O. Chandu Menon, to his proposed novel. Some of his friends, he writes in his preface to *Induleka*, did not think highly of the subject as announced: "one said, 'What is the use of taking all this trouble? If things have never taken place, what is the use of writing a story about them?'" "Others again asked me . . . how I expected to make it [the novel] a success if I described only ordinary affairs of modern life without introducing any element of the supernatural."

Kroeber, discussing his negative cases, though not with particular reference to India, remarks that evidently "a strong liking for sharp characterization, for the savor of particular events and persons, is a requisite"[5] of the novel. There are, of course, other requisites, including a sufficiently perfected prose style, and some of the factors involved in the development of the novel are institutional. But if those stressed here are indeed requisites, it would seem that some considerable degree of reorientation in the Indian world view would have had to precede or accompany the appearance of the novel in that country. Certain statements made by Priyaranjan Sen in his article, *Influence of Western Literature in the Development of the Bengali*

Novel, have relevance to this question. He is discussing the efforts of Bhudeb Mukherjee (1825–1894) and others to perpetuate the Sanskrit tradition in literature and to make use of old models in the writing of fiction. Bhudeb Mukherjee, he says, "defends the use of hyperbole so prevalent in . . . classical literature, because it contributes to the sense of wonder or the *Adbhut ras*: those who are simple by nature open themselves up to wonder at the things of the universe; hence our Purānas [legendary tales] which reflect our national spirit which is simple and pure are naturally full of hyperbole. The heroes and heroines of such Purānas are not tied to space and time, are not creatures of flesh and blood; but if you dive deep, if you seek the underlying significance, you will no more complain against the conception of such characters."[6] Seeking to explain why these efforts failed, Sen writes: "The pedantic and stilted style of most of these books went against them; there was no recognition of the fact that man as man deserved some notice from the novelist, that interest in humanity had grown up; and mythical personages pictured in Sanskrit tradition were all of noble birth—superior to, and therefore far removed from, the status and circumstances of the majority of the reading public."[7] Elsewhere, Sen notes that "new ways of viewing nature, man and God"[8] can be seen in Bengali literature. A systematic study of culture contact and culture change, with Indian world view as the focus, should advance our knowledge of acculturation processes. Literature, including fiction, provides a major source of material for such a study.

If we accept Duncan's theses that "Great literature is

the conscious exploration through the imagination of the
possibilities of human action in society,"[9] and that "Men of
letters rise to power through their ability to create symbolic roles which give expressive form to the desires,
beliefs, and values of those acting out such roles in various
phases of social action,"[10] it is obvious that to students of
Indian society and culture, Indian literature offers an
important source of materials, materials of a character
scarcely to be obtained from other sources no matter how
refined the methods of approach. Of all literature, narrative prose fiction is, I believe, of particular value because
its forms allow almost unlimited freedom. To be sure, the
use of such materials, because of their symbolic character,
is not without difficulty. As Wellek and Warren point out,
there is a danger "of taking the novel seriously in the
wrong way, that is, as a document or case history, as . . . a
confession, a true story, a history of a life and its times.
Literature must . . . of course, stand in recognizable relation to life, but the relations are very various: the life can
be heightened or burlesqued or antithesized; it is in any
case a selection, of a specifically purposive sort, from life.
We have to have a knowledge independent of literature in
order to know what the relation of a specific work to 'life'
may be."[11]

At the level of what may be termed descriptive ethnography, the difficulties of using this material are at a
minimum. There seems no reason to suppose that the
zemindar's establishment, to take a concrete example,
described by Bankim Chandra Chatterji with a wealth of
detail in *The Poison Tree* (pp. 27–44) is not a faithful
representation; or that the village school of which we are

given a glimpse in Taraknath Ganguli's *Svarnalata* (pp. 124–127) is not closely patterned upon actuality. Similarly passages describing food, costume, and various other items of material culture, as well as play and pastimes, ceremony and ritual, to give other examples, can be accepted as factually true, if often incomplete. Using the language itself, the words and phrases of the novels and short stories, one could make a study of expressions of endearment or terms of vituperation which would probably correspond closely to ordinary usage. Distortion of reality would seem to serve no useful purpose; on the contrary, verisimilitude in matters of detail heightens the novelist's effect. Descriptions by a trained ethnographer dealing with these subjects would no doubt tell us more; but, for very many parts of India, a country with great local variation, we do not have such descriptions, nor shall we ever have them for the nineteenth century, when the two novels just referred to were written, and in many cases we search in vain sources of other types for comparable information.

The novels and short stories on the accompanying list vary greatly in this respect and as a whole are not so rich in this type of material as we might wish. Of those especially noteworthy for what might be called "ethnographical" realism[12] one of the best is the novel of Lal Behari Day, *Bengal Village Life*, the prize entry in a competition for the best novel depicting Bengal village life. By and large, although there are many exceptions, notably Venu Chitale's *In Transit*, the nineteenth century novels, and those written during the first twenty-five or thirty years of this century may be mined for this type of material more profitably than those of more recent date.

In investigating institutions, interpersonal relations, attitudes and values, fiction is also of great value, but the novels and short stories must be used with caution, and it is often necessary to look behind the manifest content. The distortion may be conscious and purposive or it may be unconscious; and the reasons for this distortion, if we can discover them, help us to understand Indian society and culture, even though at the present time we can in many instances do no more than formulate hypotheses. In some cases we may be able to discern more than the author intended in his presentation. The student of the joint family, for example, should not overlook the numerous descriptions of this institution in fiction; in reading one of the best of these, Sarat Chandra Chatterji's *The Deliverance*, it is well to remember that the writer, who deals with this institution in several of his short stories,[13] wishes to emphasize the necessity, if the joint family is to survive, of subordinating personal interests to those of the group, and to do this he makes use of a dramatic, and it would seem, highly improbable dénouement. The knowledge that *The Home and the World* is, as Jadunath Sarkar has pointed out,[14] Tagore's "reply to Aurobindo Ghose," contributes to our fuller understanding of the novel and prevents us from taking the novel too literally.

A passage in *Godan* (p. 231) by Prem Chand, illustrates certain aspects of the interrelations between members of different castes and gives dramatic expression to the attitudes that lie at the base of these interrelationships. The peasant, Hori, has borrowed money from a Brahman of his village, and now after some time, the sum plus interest is greater than he can pay. Gobar, Hori's son, knows that the interest charges are greater than the law allows, and tries to persuade his father to pay less than the Brahman claims as his due. He is openly scornful of the Brahman's demands to receive the entire sum. The Brahman is speaking: ' "Make no mistake about it son. I'm a Brahmin. You won't live in peace by devouring my money. All right, I forego the seventy also. I won't go to court either. But I'm a Brahmin and I know how to get back my money. You'll come to my door and offer me the money on bended knees."

'Gobar was unperturbed. But a storm raged in Hori's mind. Had it been a Thakur's or a *Bania's* money it would not have mattered. But a Brahmin's money!

'God keep him from a Brahmin's wrath! They said if a Brahmin's wrath visited a person, not a single member of the family survived.'

This passage as it stands is a bit of ethnography which adds to my knowledge of the caste system, with particular reference to the importance, in the system, of power as a focus of evaluation. The theme appears again in *The Brahman's Curse*, one of the stories in S. B. Banerjea's *Tales of Bengal*. Also of interest to the student of caste are some remarks addressed to his reader by the author of *Induleka* (p. 76) prior to introducing a Nambudiri character: "It is necessary for me to describe in this and succeeding chapters a fickle-minded and libidinous Nambudiripad. There is, however, no class of men in Malabar for whom I entertain greater respect than I do for the Nambudiris. I am acquainted with several who are distinguished for their intellect and ability, and I am proud to reckon some of them among my intimate friends. But in every caste we see shrewdness and stupidity, wisdom and folly, side by side, and the caste of Nambudiris is no exception to the rule . . . I am confident that the intelligent and impartial reader will fully and freely absolve me from any intention of maliciously exposing to contempt and derision a section of the community which is so generally regarded with veneration and honour as are the Nambudiripads and Nambudiris in Malabar." What interests me here, in contrast to the passage from *Godan*, is not the attitudes expressed; the fact that O. Chandu Menon, a Nayar, felt it necessary or desirable to make these statements tells me something about Malabar society in the latter part of the nineteenth century, and the relations between the two castes.

It would be worthwhile, I believe, to make a study of the Indian woman in fiction. In her roles as mother, wife, and sister, she figures very largely in these novels and short stories; it is my impression that she appears less frequently as daughter. As we observe with the mind's eye this procession of devoted, submissive, faithful, loyal, self-sacrificing women, the question arises, are these characters intended as realistic portrayals? There is a certain amount of evidence to suggest that this is indeed the case, particularly with reference to the woman as mother. Bankim Chandra Chatterji, who in his own person frequently addresses his readers directly, writes in *Krishna Kanta's Will* (p. 245): "Woman is full of forgiveness, of compassion, of love; woman is the crowning excellence of God's creation, the shadow of the Gods. Man the Gods' creation only. Woman is light, man is shadow." Madan Gopal, discussing the work of Prem Chand, writes:

"Woman is the pivotal point, the sheet-anchor of a happy domestic life—the only foundation of a stable social order. She is the bedrock of society. Far from being the equal of man, she is his superior. Her responsibilities are truly gigantic, because she holds the privileged position of mother.

"Prem Chand always saw the mother in woman, for in her capacity of a mother she is capable of great self-denial and self-sacrifice . . ."[15] And again, "All these noble qualities of self-denial, self-sacrifice, self-control, and the capacity to rise to super-human heights when occasion demands, are typical of the Indian woman. When she finds her husband in trouble, she would sacrifice her all. And, for this reason, Premchand had nothing but praise for her."[16] Ela Sen, in her foreword to *Darkening Days*, pays her tribute to Indian womanhood: "Out of the ghastly panorama there emerged one beauty—motherhood . . . untiring energy, undaunted love and greatness character-ized these simple peasant women who had become destitute of all wordly possessions." (p. 17) "The gaunt and spectral mother . . . epitomized the spirit of Bengal's women—undaunted and alive in the midst of death—pure as a flame amongst garbage." (p. 18)

Unless we are to assume that these qualities are in fact characteristic of Indian women, that the great demands made upon them from an early age by society, do or did produce women possessing the virtues attributed to them —and, remembering particularly Ramabai Ranade's auto-biography, I am not inclined to rule this out as a possibility —we should seek to discover why women in certain roles must be so highly idealized. It seems clear that in the case

of woman as wife we are dealing with a literary tradition:
Sita, Savitri, Sakuntala, serve as models, and at the vernacular level, in Bengal, for example, Behula, Malanchamala,
and various others.[17] A careful and detailed examination of
the material may reveal some significant regional variations in both modern and traditional literatures in this
respect. For Bengal, at any rate, there is literary con-
tinuity. What is the reason for this persistence? It is not
my intention to attempt an answer, but there may be some
connection with the ambivalence towards women observable in other areas of the culture.

At any rate, these women exemplify the ideal, and thus
express the society's values. Further, they serve as models
and as such exert an influence on living men and women.
K. C. S. in his introduction to Sarat Chandra Chatterji's
novel, *Srikanta*, says of one of the female characters, "the
hold that Annada had, and probably still has, on the
imagination of Bengal's youth . . . can hardly be overestimated." We note, too, that women occupying certain
statuses are not idealized to the same extent. The husband's
sister, and the husband's brother's wife are sometimes
permitted to appear in an unfavorable light; the step-
mother and mother-in-law are frequently malicious and
cruel. The widow, when the author is a propagandist for
social reform, is often virtuous and long-suffering, but
there is another widow, particularly in the early years of
our period, the temptress and evil-doer, who seems to owe
much to the traditional attitudes towards her as a creature
of ill-omen and a cause of anxiety.

There is much material for a study of the Indian peasant
in fiction. How realistic and true to life are the pictures

presented seems to be open to question. There appear to
be several, not incompatible, stereotypes of the peasant
which might well affect perception and result in selection in
presentation. One of them is delineated in passages from
Tagore's *Glimpses of Bengal*: "I feel a great tenderness
for the peasant folk— our ryots—big, helpless, infantile
children of Providence, who must have food brought to
their very lips, or they are undone. When the breasts of
Mother Earth dry up, they are at a loss what to do, and
can only cry. But no sooner is their hunger satisfied then
they forget all their past sufferings." (pp. 102–3) "Sometimes one or other of our simple, devoted, old ryots comes
in to see me—and their worshipful homage is so un-
affected! How much greater than I are they in the beautiful
sincerity of their reverence . . . A meek and radiantly
simple soul shines through their worn and wrinkled, old
bodies. Little children are merely simple, they have not
the unquestioning, unwavering devotion of these." (p.
104) The letters, extracts from which compose these
Glimpses, were written while Tagore was living and
travelling in the rural districts of Bengal during the years
1885–95. What, if any, were the antecedents of Tagore's
peasant, it would be interesting to know. Thompson,
mentioning his "enthusiasm for the peasant," comments,
"In a general way, he must have been aware of Tolstoy's
teaching, which was permeating the world; but there was
little conscious borrowing, only unconscious kinship of
mind . . ."[18] I think we can assume that many following
Tagore saw with his eyes. More than fifty years later Ela
Sen, for example, in the introduction to her *Darkening Days*
speaks of "simple, trusting peasant hearts."

Closely related is the villager who exemplifies India's traditional virtues and preserves a way of life no longer to be observed in towns and cities: "A few at least of India's men and women still know the Truth and worship it. These are the real and genuine Indians who live in the poor little villages and the humble towns, and earn a meagre but enjoyable living by tilling its soil. These you may still find gathered on the banks of India's holy waters, greeting the bright sun at dawn with sweet Rig-Vedic hymns, or you may see them crowding the corridors of their temples when, their day's task finished, they go to offer formal prayers to the Deity whose name has been on their lips all day."[19] This peasant seems to be connected with a kind of primitivism, a desire for the simple life, and a belief in Ram Raj as India's former condition and true goal. We are not surprised to find that the way of life of the city dweller is sometimes, as in *Murugan the Tiller*, by K. S. Venkataramani, contrasted with this idyllic existence. A wise and saintly character in Bhabani Bhattacharya's novel, *So Many Hungers!* (p. 30) says, "I am proud of my people. They are not bright and knowing and—civilized!—like you citybreds, but they are good people. Centuries of brute hardship and strain have not destroyed their faith in human values." The views attributed to Prem Chand by Gopal are shared by others: "Premchand thought that the middle class in India, the result of the impact of the West, was thoroughly corrupt, that it depended for its safety upon foreign bayonets and that its standards of moral and social values were entirely false, enveloped in artificiality and show. Against the manifold ills of this social order and its mainstay, the modern educational system, Premchand carries on a crusade."[20] A component element in this picture of the peasant is the idea that it is the village and its people which persist. A passage towards the end of *Conflict* (pp. 154–5), by Aamir Ali, expresses this: "The real people of India, the real life of India. Shankar saw that against the background of centuries and centuries: holding fast together; indestructible. And he felt proud to belong to such a people . . ."

Another peasant, who may be called the man with the hoe, makes his appearance early, and is still to be met with in fiction. We may trace him to the stereotype—which as in the other types fiction has no doubt done much to create and perpetuate—of the peasant bowed with the weight of centuries, over-burdened, poverty-stricken, victimized by landlords and money-lenders, helpless in the face of social convention, a prey to superstition, doomed to ultimate defeat by the forces arrayed against him.

Although I have noted these three stereotypes separately, they might better be considered as three aspects of a single stereotype. The relative emphasis placed on one or other of these aspects in fiction would probably be found to vary with the general theme of the author, and according, in some degree, to the period in which the work was written.

Novels and short stories furnish material for a study of the beliefs and ideas regarding the Indian character held by the people themselves. These ideas, closely related to the values and goals of the group as a whole, are often directly expressed in fiction. One example may be found in *Padmini* (p. 197), an historical novel by T. Ramakrishnan.

A wise old man of Chingleput is contrasting the British
in the person of Francis Day with the Indians: "As
for the English, I see from the reports I hear of the
Englishman who visited your court recently, about his
proud bearing and dignified demeanour, that they are
proud too, and that he belongs to a nation whose pride
and manliness and courage and chivalry will prevent them
from mingling freely with us who possess other virtues no
less important. Dogged stubbornness, endurance, an in-
tense desire to help the weak against the strong, and to
grant equality of political rights to those who are not as
physically great as themselves, these masculine virtues
usually characterize such nations. On the other hand, we
possess the softer virtues of humility, mildness, forbear-
ance, kindness, and mercy to all living things on earth.
These virtues of a sentimental kind characterize our race.
We have an individuality and an exclusiveness, the result,
of course, of our deep religious convictions, which pre-
clude us from commingling with other races."

Related ideas are expressed in *The Prince of Destiny*, by
Sarath Kumar Ghosh (p. 483). It is written with reference
to the hero that "In yielding up the resentment he was
Eastern; in the thought of the universal peace, universal
goodwill, and the brotherhood of man . . . he was Eastern.
Yes, even if the East ever possessed the greater arms, it
would make for peace and goodwill and brotherhood by
rebuking the disturber, the usurper, and the international
robber. The East only sought to live and let live." Later
on, addressing his people, the hero says: ". . . India
shall impose her will upon the world—peace. She will
range herself on the side of the weak ones of the earth,

and check the disturbers of peace, the pirates and marauders among nations." (p. 597)

Mulk Raj Anand in *Untouchable* (pp. 124–5) puts into the mouth of a poet a speech describing other aspects of the Indian character: "It is India's genius to accept all things . . . Right in the tradition of those who accepted the world and produced the baroque exhuberance of Indian architecture and sculpture, with its profound sense of form, its solidity and its mass, we will accept and work the machine. But we will do so consciously. We can see through the idiocy of these Europeans who deified money . . . we can steer clear of the pitfalls, because we have the advantage of a race-consciousness six thousand years old, a race-consciousness which accepted all the visible and invisible values. We know life. We know its secret flow. We have danced to its rhythms. We have loved it, not sentimentally through personal feelings, but pervasively, stretching ourselves outwards so far, oh, so far, that life seemed to have no limits, that miracles seemed possible . . . We cannot go wrong. Our enslavers muddle through things. We can see things clearly. We will go the whole hog with regard to machines while they nervously fumble their way with the steam-engine. And we will keep our heads through it all. We will not become slaves to gold. We can be trusted to see life steadily and see it whole."

A view of the Indian people from another angle, perhaps not now, or not ever, to the forefront in their own minds, is quite clearly a product of political circumstances, but it reflects also the Indians as viewed by the British. In *The Home and The World* (p. 41) Tagore attributes this view to Nikhil, a character who seems to come close to representing Tagore's own opinions: "Where our minds are free we find ourselves lost. Our moribund vitality must have for its rider either some fantasy, or someone in authority, or a sanction from the pundits, in order to make it move. So long as we are impervious to truth and have to be moved by some hypnotic stimulus, we must know that we lack the capacity for self-government. Whatever may be our condition, we shall either need some imaginary ghost or some actual medicine-man to terrorise over us." Tagore has developed this theme in one of the allegorical sketches included in *The Parrot's Training and Other Stories*.

There is also a regional dimension to what we may think of as national character viewed from the inside. Mohan Singh, for example, gives us a conception of the Punjabi character which is probably not idiosyncratic (cf. p. 36). The general subject might be further pursued by means of a study of fictional characters.

Many of the ideas which appear to be now firmly established probably grew up as part of the reaction to British contact. The extent to which this is the case, and how much if anything they owe to British and European writers might well be investigated. At any rate, the beliefs and ideas held by Indians regarding their own character are of considerable importance from more than one angle; they are central, for example, to a study of the Indian world view, and to an understanding of political developments, both past and present.

Political events and issues of our hundred year period are reflected in various ways, both direct and indirect, in the literature. The terrorist movement in Bengal in the early years of this century, the civil disobedience campaigns of the Indian National Congress, Partition and its aftermath, are drawn upon for plot and character by many of the novelists and short-story writers. To the student of Indian politics, however, fiction is chiefly valuable as revealing attitudes towards events and towards political theories and personalities.

The historical novels can perhaps most fruitfully be considered in this connection. Borrowed from the West, the genre had a vogue in India during the first fifty years or so of our period, but appears to have lost favor in more recent years. Even with such models as Scott and others provided, and at least some source materials, Indian authors were not, if we can judge from the examples available to the English reader, primarily interested in creating a realistic picture of the people and society of a bygone day. The historical novel seems to be an offshoot of the growth of nationalism, an expression of a newly-awakened pride in India's past glories, a means of arousing and fostering the desire for self-government. There was some risk in using the Mutiny for this purpose, but the struggles of the Hindus against the Muslims did not meet with the same objection. Hence the prominence of Sivaji and Pratap Singh in literature. Thompson says of Tagore's *Katha*, stories (in verse) "chiefly of Buddhist times and the Sikh and Maratha efforts and the Rajput struggle to keep independence," that they "must be regarded as a very effective part of his political propaganda."[21] That fiction, and other forms of literature, deserve serious study by those concerned with the development of political thought and activity in India is indicated by a statement of Guha-Thakurta: "The political events that preceded the Svadeśi movement would in themselves have been wholly insufficient to bring about the new nationalistic consciousness if they had not been reinforced by a growing tendency towards the literary expression of patriotic ideals and sentiments."[22]

The novel throughout its history in India has served the purposes of social as well as political reform; so also the short story. J. C. Ghosh, quoting the English preface to the first edition of Piari Chand Mitra's novel, states that it "is a cautionary tale written with the primary object of showing 'the pernicious effects of allowing children to be improperly brought up.' "[23] Bankim Chandra Chatterji, though not a reformer in the ordinary sense of the word— he has been characterized as a "pugnacious controversialist in defense of Hindu culture"[24]—was critical of "the fraility and defects of his own countrymen"[25] and in various ways his views are reflected in his work.[26] Some writers had a more limited objective. Not all are as explicit in this respect as O. Chandu Menon, who writes in the introduction to *Induleka*: "My narrative of the love and courtship of Madhavan is intended to show to the young ladies of Malabar how happy they can be if they have the freedom to choose their partners, and how supremely enjoyable a thing it would be for a young educated lady, at a time when she attains a marriageable age, to observe, to study, to admire and love a well-educated, handsome young man of unblemished moral character like Madhavan, who becomes first her companion and friend, gets closer and closer in friendship, and finally falls in love with her, adoring her as the source of all his happiness in this world, as the person without whom he does not care to live, and for whose happiness he would sacrifice everything in his power. Alliances arising out of such pure, sweet, reciprocal love only deserve to be called marriages, and it is my earnest desire that this should be the way in which the Nair ladies, who already enjoy much greater freedom in respect of matrimony than other Hindu women, should take their husbands." Other writers attack the dowry system, the prohibition of the marriage of widows, child marriage, the general position of women in Hindu society. A systematic survey of the material would, I believe, reveal less concern with reforms in the caste system than might be expected. It is my impression that, as we might predict, during the last twenty years or so political rather than social aims have predominated. The remarks made by Gopal concerning Prem Chand would apply equally well to many others : "Premchand was a writer with a purpose and wanted to train the masses for a struggle. To that end his works abound in heroes and patriots, inspired by noble ideals, loving, truthful, sacrificing, and always upholding the cause of the oppressed."[27] Krishan Chandar, according to Mohamed Sadiq, "feels that he has a mission as a short story writer—to show up the capitalist and the ruling classes in all their brutality and bestiality."[28]

The strong didactic tone characteristic of much of Indian fiction has been noted by Anand and Iqbal, and in their discussion of the Indian short story they trace it to the ancient literary tradition of India : the stories, according to these authors, "still retain a significant, if increasingly tenuous link with the old fables and folk narratives, which

accounts for their obsessive didactic strain."[29] It appears
probable that other factors are involved and that in the
early years at any rate Indian authors were influenced by
Victorian moralistic works, and also that consideration
should be given to the general spirit of the times: an
influential section of the population had come, largely as a
result of contact with the West, to be sharply critical of
many Indian institutions, to press in various ways the
need for reform; new and revolutionary ideas could be
presented in palatable form in the novels and short
stories.

The discussion so far has been concerned with descriptive content, but investigation of certain technical aspects
of fiction might also prove rewarding. With style we
cannot be concerned. A number of the works available in
English are translations, and very few of the Indian
novelists who wrote originally in English have had suffi-
cient control over the language to bend it to their purposes;
the outstanding exception is R. K. Narayan who has
developed a style almost perfectly coordinated with his
subject matter. But a study of characterization might prove
suggestive and lead to the formulation of useful hypotheses.
Is there anything regarding the mode of characterization
that can be said to be typical of Indian fiction generally,
which can distinguish it from other literatures? On the
basis of what is known concerning acculturation we might
expect to find some distinctive features. Anand and Iqbal,
discussing the Indian short story, have perhaps put a finger
on such a trait: "The significant feature of the Western
short story is the subtle interplay, indeed interpenetration,
of situation and character which produces the climax and

leads to the ultimate dénouement. But in most Indian stories these two elements of the theme are very sharply differentiated; there is little interplay, and what we witness is a series of collisions which seem to set up an unresolved crisis . . . It may well be that the background of life with which they [the Indian writers] have to deal does not lend itself to the same kind of formal treatment as the material with which the European writers are concerned."[30] It is my impression that these remarks apply equally well to the novel, in which the characters often have a static quality, do not develop, and are mere instruments in the plot. If this should prove, on analysis, to be typically the case, it would be worthwhile to consider the differences in the "background of life" which make it difficult, or undesirable, or impossible for Indians to copy their models in this respect.

A part, perhaps a large part, of the "background" of the European writers is the idea, very old in Western thought, that character is destiny, that what a man is as an individual, and what he does, what happens to him, are closely linked. The absence of such assumptions in Indian thought may partially account for the characteristic features noted by Anand and Iqbal. In Western fiction character is largely delineated by means of incident. Wellek and Warren, observing the close relationship between plot and characterization, quote Henry James, who asks in *The Art of Fiction*, "What is character but the determination of incident? What is incident but the illustration of character?"[31] If these two are conceived as more or less unrelated, characterization becomes a technical problem. I am inclined to consider it a possibility that the lack of a

close interrelationship in Indian conceptualization may be
one reason for the cardboard quality of the characters in so
many of the novels and short stories.

There is another possibility. It was suggested earlier in
this paper that a lack of interest in human nature and
individual character may have hindered the development
of the novel in India, and perhaps the interest is still not
very great. A character in fiction is real, writes Forster,
"when the novelist knows everything about it. He may not
choose to tell us all he knows . . . But he will give us the
feeling that though the character has not been explained,
it is explicable . . ."[32] With a few exceptions, it must be
said of Indian novelists and short story-writers in general,
as Sayyid Abdul Laṭif said of Urdu writers: "None of
them . . . reveals a deep and discriminating study of
human nature." He adds that "their observations are
necessarily limited by their inadequate knowledge and
perception."[33]

Certain sociological factors may be relevant to a consideration of the general problem. The individual in
Indian society is to a large extent subordinated to the
group and does not assume the significance granted to
him in the West. In this connection some remarks by
B. K. Mallik are of interest: "To the Hindu the individual
as bare individual never appealed apart from his relation-
ships. He understood him, if at all, as only a member or
constituent of a society or group, or organization. To him
the essence of individuality lay in the unity which the
multiple individuals constituting a group or society are
bound to profess. If in spite of all that he did not succeed
in getting rid of him altogether, his very last act was to

give him the chance of absorption or immolation in the divine absolute as if that consummation would appease the most baffling of all aspirations, individuality . . ."[34] Also, role-expectations are highly specific and institutionalized to a degree not found in the West. It would seem to follow that the individual is viewed primarily as a player of roles and that his distinctive personal characteristics receive less attention than the manner in which he meets the expectations of his roles as defined by the society. There is a strong tendency to attribute qualities to the individual by virtue of the status which he occupies, and his experiences are in many cases capable of explanation in terms of his status. In *Srikanta*, by Sarat Chandra Chatterji, the hero on one occasion remains for some time alone at night in the cremation grounds, and later gives an account of his experiences to a company of people: "After I had finished no one spoke for some time: there was silence throughout the tent. At length the elderly gentleman heaved a deep sigh, and placing a hand on my shoulder, said with impressive slowness, 'Babu-ji, you have been able to return with your life; that is because you are a true Brahmin; nobody else could have done it . . . I touch the feet of your forefathers a thousand million times; it is their spiritual merit that saved you last night.' And in his emotion he put his hand on my feet." (p. 117) Power of a particular kind, we know from older literary sources, accrued to the individual who fulfilled his role-expectations *perfectly* and perhaps we are not too fanciful if we discern in the above passage some hint or reflection or extension of this idea; at any rate, what impresses the old man is not the bravery or courage of Srikanta as an individual.

The nature, furthermore, of interpersonal relations is determined to an extent greater than in the West by the statuses occupied by the participants. The body of fiction contains many examples of this with reference to caste and the family. One of the most striking is to be found in *Ratanbai*, by S. M. Nikambé: a young girl, married only a short time before, is brought, a widow, to the home of her deceased husband's brother; in her position as wife she had been an object of consideration and made much of by all; now she is reviled, and for a time not even asked to enter the house. An elderly member of the household says to the widow's brother-in-law, "The wretch has swallowed up our Dinu! Why did she marry him? To eat him up this way! Why hast thou brought this ill-luck into the house? She will surely swallow someone here. Our Dinu is gone and she is nothing to us now." (p. 35) Later on, when another death in the family occurs, this woman says to the widow, "You have brought this ill-luck, and you have been the cause of our misery." (p. 82)

In another novel, *The Dark Dancer*, by Balachandra Rajan, the hero reflects upon his own background, "where the map of one's life was drawn even before one's first cry", as contrasted with that of his English friend: "All the emotions and responsibilities were systematically charted—to the village, to the government, to the complex yet precise hierarchy of the joint family, the relation of man to society, man to man, even the relation of a man to his wife, so that all that remained for private definition was the deep, personal mystery of a man's relation to God. And even that mystery was set in a ceremony and process rigidly prescribed to the minutest detail, so that, while the discovery was one's own, the only possible way was that of all men." (p. 162)

A clue to related psychological factors is perhaps to be found in certain personality characteristics of Indians, and some statements of Carstairs in a recent book are at least worth bearing in mind. In a brief statement concerning the respects in which the subjects of his study appeared to him to resemble each other and to differ from his "conception of the Western norm," he noted that, "They displayed an apparent lack of empathy with regard to each other's feelings; and their fellows' motives seemed to them ever arbitrary, inscrutable and suspect . . . Interpersonal relations tended to be on a superficial level . . ." He adds that, "In contrast to this, they acted with the greatest self-assurance when observing the formalities of an elaborate social etiquette, or when impersonally executing the duties associated with their respective caste roles . . ."[35]

Carstairs' study was localized, and the number of his subjects was small; he himself points out that his generalizations may or may not be found to hold for India as a whole. But it might also be noted in connection with our problem that Taylor has remarked upon a lack of concern with personal qualities in Hinduism, the system which establishes the relationship of man with god. "Hinduism," he says, "has little place in its system for personal qualities which cannot be reduced to conceptual terms, or for personal relations that cannot be interpreted in ceremonial forms. It has taken the alternative, and has developed its religious attitudes in abstract conceptual, and in concrete ceremonial, forms. It has related religion in the most intimate manner to philosophical thought on the one hand,

and to a type of social organization on the other. This is paralleled by an emphasis on right knowledge and on correct action as alternative methods of obtaining salvation. The channelings of religious interests in these two forms is made possible by the relative isolation of intangible personal qualities from the field of spiritually significant things."[36]

The relationship between national character and literature must be, if any, indirect and very complex, and in the present state of our knowledge of Indian character and personality it is daring even to speculate. But it may be possible one day to discover the reasons why Mrs. Gertrude Emerson Sen's plea for a "penetrating psychological analysis [in fiction] of true Indian types"[37] has so far gone unanswered.

Whatever the main focus of our interest in Indian fiction, the question arises as to how representative is the body of material available in English. The accompanying list has been compiled, not very systematically, over a period of years. While it is not exhaustive, I believe that it is a fair sample of fiction written originally in English or translated into English. The volume of material in the various vernaculars is of course very much greater. Any hypotheses formulated on the basis of this type of material must be tested by other methods of study, but the worth of these literary sources, particularly for certain of the purposes which I have tried to indicate, depends on whether or not we can fairly assume that there are not substantial differences between the documents available in English and those in the vernacular languages. Some Indian critics hold that writers of fiction in English are to be distinguished from those who write in the vernaculars. An editorial in *Quest* offers an explanation for the differences perceived: "There is a growing feeling among our writers that Indo-Anglican literature, especially fiction, continues to achieve a *succes d'estime* which hides its inevitable sophistication of the reality of Indian life. What is wrong with these overestimated novelists is not that they do not know the craft—in fact, they know more of it than do their vernacular counterparts—but that they receive experience on the surface, with the romantic expectation of turning it into a commodity acceptable to Western readers hungry for an exotic revelation of the East."[38] If this is true, we must indeed handle our material cautiously. But I believe that there is reason to doubt the general applicability of this statement. A few writers must be considered exceptions, but for the most part I do not see marked differences between the works on the list published in translation, which are approximately one-fourth of the total, and those written in English. The problem, however, remains, and deserves further attention by those who can utilize sources in one or more of the vernaculars.

A question also exists with regard to regional differences. Although all of India shares a common literary tradition there are variations at the vernacular level which correspond more or less closely to the linguistic areas. We should, therefore, not be surprised to find that Marathi fiction, to take one example, had some features which distinguished it from that in other vernaculars. Also, the general social and cultural heritage is not identical for all parts of India. Furthermore, it is not likely that writers of fiction in one vernacular exerted much

influence on those of another since the languages are
mutually unintelligible, and the works of very few writers
in one have been translated into others; contact has been
generally, if at all, through the medium of English.

Indian critics have in some cases considered it possible
to discern and describe characteristic features of particular
vernacular literatures. Mohan Singh, for example, writes
of his own Punjabi language and literature: "Panjabi is the
composite language of a composite people, the basis of
whose structure is agricultural, and the superstructure
military. Both the rustic and the soldier are as free of heart
as of speech; their one object is self-expression, self-
assertion; nothing is for them too sacrosanct, too beautiful
and delicate, too useful or valuable to be rough-handled,
changed, exploited; for both, freedom and immediate full
utility are the first loves and the last; they both keep to or
find their level, and are anxious to labour, to strike and
then seek escape, comfort and consolation in song, dance,
drink, sexual enjoyment, sallies of wit and humour and
sarcasm, and generally in excess. When they give they
give generously, of money, of loyalty and friendship, of
blood and bone; when they take they wrest mercilessly.
These characteristics of the Panjab Jat, Rajput, Ahir and
Gujjar, one finds amply evidenced in literary work by Jats
themselves, in folk songs, in tribal and national wars
recorded in history, in the witness of oral tradition. And
these characteristics of men and women have their corres-
ponding equivalents in the speech they utter, the literature
they compose or pen."[39] Was it perhaps these characteristics which impressed a non-Punjabi, K. Nagarajan, who
wrote of Mulk Raj Anand, "He sees life in the raw and

exposes it mercilessly, flesh, wounds, blood and all . . . shedding sentimentalism, [he] writes with a fine touch of scorn of the social and economic inequalities which to him make a mockery of much of Indian life . . ."?[40]

There may be subtle differences which would reveal distinctive aspects of the attitudes towards life of the writers and the people for whom the books were written. Edward Thompson, who knew Bengali literature very well, wrote in an article on *Some Vernacular Characteristics of Bengali Literature*,[41] that "irony is so prevalent in Bengali literature that it may almost be called the differentia of the literature. You often get whole books in which almost every sentence has a veiled meaning." Gangadhar Gadgil, the Marathi short-story writer, tells me that Gujaratis comment on the amount of humor in Marathi fiction.

Unfortunately, although all but one, Gujarati, of the major vernacular literatures of India are represented on the accompanying list by authors who wrote originally in English or whose works have been translated, the distribution is very uneven. Bengali writers form the largest single group, comprising approximately one-third of the total. This is probably to be expected, and is connected with the growth of Calcutta as the intellectual capital of India. For the other literatures, the sample is inadequate for comparative purposes.

In this list, fiction has been given a fairly wide meaning. A few sketches or volumes of sketches have been included which do not, strictly speaking, fall into the category of either the novel or the short story. The autobiographies number forty-five, but the line between fiction and autobiography is actually not easy to draw. Several of the works classed as novels clearly are or appear to be autobiographical; where either is the case it is indicated in the notes so far as the information permits. Some selection has been exercised in regard to the autobiographical material. A good deal of this type of literature is of interest mainly to students of Indian politics, and items of this sort which appear in the bibliography on *Government and Politics of India and Pakistan*[42] prepared by Patrick Wilson are omitted. I have, however, listed certain works of a similar nature which are not included in Wilson's bibliography. Although the discussion has been confined to fiction, in many respects autobiography can be put to similar use, and these personal documents, even when they are quite impersonal records, if we penetrate deeply, show us the ways in which individuals reacted to experience and viewed the life of their times.[43]

NOTES AND REFERENCES

[1] The title of the English translation is *The Spoilt Child*.

[2] Cf. J. C. Ghosh, *Bengali Literature*, London: Oxford University Press, 1948, Chapter IV.

[3] The article is reprinted in A. L. Kroeber, *The Nature of Culture*, The University of Chicago Press [1952], p. 413.

[4] S. K. De, *History of Bengali Literature in the Nineteenth Century*. 1800–1825. University of Calcutta Press, 1919, pp. 445–446.

[5] Kroeber, p. 415.

[6] The article is published in the *Journal of the Department of Letters*, Vol. XXII, University of Calcutta, Calcutta University Press, 1932, pp. 1–76; p. 14.

[7] *Op. cit.*, p. 15.

[8] Priyaranjan Sen, *Western Influence in Bengali Literature*, University of Calcutta, 1932, p. 385.

[9] Hugh Dalziel Duncan, *Language and Literature in Society, A Sociological Essay on Theory and Method in the Interpretation of Linguistic Symbols, With a Bibliographical Guide to the Sociology of Literature*. The University of Chicago Press [1953], p. 1.

[10] Duncan, p. 2.

[11] René Wellek and Austin Warren, *Theory of Literature*, New York: Harcourt, Brace [1949], p. 219.

[12] I have borrowed this term from D. S. Mirsky, *A History of Russian Literature*, Comprising *A History of Russian Literature* and *Contemporary Russian Literature*, Edited and abridged by Francis J. Whitfield. New York: Knopf, 1949, p. 233.

[13] Cf. S. C. Sen Gupta, *Sarat Chandra: Man and Artist.*
Calcutta, Saraswaty Library [1945], Chapter III.

[14] In the *Modern Review*, Vol. XXVI, November, 1919.

[15] Madan Gopal, *Premchand*, Lahore: The Bookabode
[1944], p. 39.

[16] Gopal, p. 41.

[17] For Behula cf. the story of Manasa-Mangala in Dinesh
Chandra Sen, *History of the Bengali Language and
Literature*, Calcutta: Published by the University,
1911, pp. 257–276. For Malanchamala cf. Dinesh
Chandra Sen, *Folk Literature of Bengal*, Published by
the University of Calcutta, 1920, pp. 267–322. Sen,
commenting on the tale, writes: "Here in this land
women have always evinced a high spirit of sacrifice
at the altar of domestic love, and their self-immola-
tion on the funeral pyre of their husbands and
practice of austere *Brahmacharya*, have evoked wonder
of all unprejudiced minds. In this country Mālañ-
chamālā is no day-dream of poets, no idealistic or
unrealistic mental phantom 'without human interest',
simply because the human being in this case happens
to possess a super-human strength of soul." (p. 335)

[18] Edward Thompson, *Rabindranath Tagore, Poet and
Dramatist*, London [etc.] Oxford University Press,
1926, p. 157.

[19] Mulk Raj Anand, *The Hindu View of Art*, with an introductory essay on Art and Reality by Eric Gill.
London: George Allen and Unwin [1933], p. 218.

[20] Gopal, p. 36.

[21] Thompson, p. 166.

[22] P. Guha-Thakurta, *The Bengali Drama, Its Origin and
Development*. London: Kegan Paul, Trench, Trübner,
1930, p. 148. Cf. pp. 149–150 for his comments on

the novels of Bankim Chandra Chatterji and Romesh
Chandra Dutt in this connection.

23 Ghosh, p. 127.

24 M. M. Bhattacharjee, "Bankimchandra Chatterjee," in
Great Men of India, L. F. Rushbrook Williams, ed.
The Home Library Club, The Times of India—The
Statesman, Associated Newspapers of Ceylon, n.d.,
p. 548.

25 Bhattacharjee, p. 548.

26 Cf. Jayanta Kumar Das Gupta, *A Critical Study of the
Life and Novels of Bankimchandra*. Published by the
Calcutta University, 1937. Chapter XVII.

27 Gopal, p. 50.

28 Mohamed Sadiq, *Twentieth-Century Urdu Literature* (*A
Review*), Baroda: Padmaja Publications [1947], p.
81.

29 In their introduction to *Indian Short Stories*, p. 8.

30 Cf. introduction to *Indian Short Stories*, p. 8.

31 Wellek and Warren, p. 224.

32 E. M. Forster, *Aspects of the Novel*. New York: Harcourt, Brace [1954], p. 63.

33 Sayyid Abdul Laṭīf, *The Influence of English Literature
on Urdu Literature*. London: Forster Groom, 1924,
p. 124.

34 B. K. Mallik, *The Individual and the Group, An Indian
Study in Conflict*. London: George Allen and Unwin
[1939], pp. 103–104.

35 G. Morris Carstairs, *The Twice-Born, A study of a
Community of High-Caste Hindus*. London: The
Hogarth Press, 1957, p. 106.

36 W. S. Taylor, "Changing Attitudes in a Conflict of
Cultures." *Character and Personality*, Vol. 10, 1941,
p. 105.

[37] Mrs. Sen was addressing the First All-India Writers' Conference. Cf. *Indian Writers in Council, Proceedings of the First All-India Writers' Conference (Jaipur, 1945)*, K. R. Srinivasa Iyengar, ed. Bombay: The International Book House, p. 77.

[38] Vol. II, No. 5, April–May, 1957.

[39] Mohan Singh, *An Introduction to Panjabi Literature*. Amritsar: Nanak Singh Pustak Mala [1951?], p. 257.

[40] K. Nagarajan, "The Development of the Novel in India." *Art and Letters, The Journal of the Royal India and Pakistan Society*, Vol. XXIII, No. 1, 1949, p. 44.

[41] *Indian Art and Letters*, n.s. Vol. 1, No. 1, 1927, p. 11.

[42] *Government and Politics of India and Pakistan, 1885–1955: A Bibliography of Works in Western Languages*. Compiled and edited by Patrick Wilson. Berkeley: University of California, South Asia Studies, Institute of East Asiatic Studies.

[43] Cf. Gordon W. Allport, *The Use of Personal Documents in Psychological Science*. Social Science Research Council, Bulletin 49, 1942, and Louis Gottschalk, Clyde Kluckhohn, Robert Angell, *The Use of Personal Documents in History, Anthropology, and Sociology*. Social Science Research Council, Bulletin 53, 1945.

An Annotated List of Fiction and Autobiography Written by Indians in English or Translated into English

AUTHORS are entered in the list under the last name except for South Indians, in which cases, in accordance with general usage, the penultimate element in the name is used for purposes of entry. The spelling of Indian names presents some problems to the bibliographer. Different works of a single author often appear under various spellings of his name. In such cases I have arbitrarily selected one. In a few cases, where the final element in the name is omitted from the title page, I have put in parenthesis the name as it appears on the publication.

Because of the difficulties involved in establishing the chronological order in which the books of individual writers were published originally, and the difficulties are very great in the case of authors who wrote and published originally in Indian languages, the separate works of individual authors are listed alphabetically, except where collections of short stories are annotated together, and where two or more volumes form a chronological series annotated as a whole.

For a few items on the list my information is incomplete. Nevertheless, when reasonably certain that such works have been published in English, I have included them.

With very few exceptions I have examined those books on the list which are cataloged in the National Union Catalog in the Library of Congress. In annotating, I have occasionally quoted statements or opinions not my own when I have been able to examine the book; for the notes of books which I have not been able to see, I have where possible given some indication of the contents by quoting a critic or reviewer. The works referred to in the notes by the name of the author are:

J. C. Ghosh, *Bengali Literature*. London: Oxford University Press, 1948.

S. C. Sen Gupta, *Sarat Chandra, Man and Artist*. Calcutta: Saraswaty Library [1945].

Bhupal Singh, *A Survey of Anglo-Indian Fiction*. London: Oxford University Press, 1954.

K. R. Srinivasa Iyengar, *The Indian Contribution to English Literature*. Bombay: Karnatak Publishing House, 1945.

In preparing the list I was fortunate in having the assistance of Dr. Horace I. Poleman and Mr. Walter Maurer of the Orientalia Division, The Library of Congress; members of the staff of the library of the University of Pennsylvania; and of the New York Public Library. I gratefully acknowledge also my debt to Dr. Richard L. Park, who kindly checked a number of titles, not to be found in the National Union Catalog, in the British Museum and the India Office Library.

ABBAS, Khwaja Ahmad, *Blood and Stones*. Bombay: Hind
  Kitabs [1947] 48 p.
Communal riots in Bombay.

Cages of Freedom and other Stories. Bombay: Hind Kitabs
  [1952] 106 p.
Ten stories; the title story is a fable for our times;
others have to do with partition and its aftermath; the
conflict between father and son is the theme of another.

Defeat for Death; A Story Without Names. Baroda:
  Padmaja, 1944.

Inquilab. Bombay: Jaico Publishing House [1955] 392 p.
The period of this novel is 1919–1932, and the plot is
interwoven with the political events of that time; for the
most part the scene is North India—Delhi and Aligarh;
the chief character is portrayed as a boy growing up in a
Muslim family, and later as a student at Aligarh.

*One Thousand Nights on a Bed of Stones, and Other
  Stories*. Bombay: Jaico Publishing House [1957]
  173 p.

Rice, and Other Stories. With an introductory letter by
  Mulk Raj Anand. Bombay: Kutub [1947] 167 p.
Ten stories: a mother, an Anglo-Indian nurse, a couple
of prostitutes, a young revolutionary, and others figure
in these stories; one is laid in Kashmir, several in
Bombay, one in a North Indian village.

Son of India.

Tomorrow is Ours. Delhi: Rajkamal Publications, 1946.
  168 p.
The love story of two "modern" Indians during the
second world war; tale has socio-political overtones.

ALI, Aamir, *Conflict*. Bombay: National Information and
   Publications [1947] 167 p.
   According to summary on the flyleaf: "The story
   vividly portrays the reactions of . . . a sensitive village
   youth who goes to college in Bombay. Through him is
   revealed the travail of a generation exposed to opposing
   forces, torn between village and city, old and new, East
   and West. The story culminates in the dramatic events
   of 1942." The village, in Maharashtra (?), wins out,
   but a relatively small part of the book is devoted to
   it. The hero, and most of the other characters are
   Hindus.

ALI, Ahmed, *Twilight in Delhi*. London: The Hogarth
   Press, 1940. 319 p.
   Life and death in an upper-class Muslim family in Delhi
   during the first two decades of this century; considerable ethnography.

ANAND, Mulk Raj, *The Barber's Trade Union and Other
   Stories*. London: J. Cape [1944] 175 p.
   The Tractor and the Corn Goddess and Other Stories.
   Bombay: Thacker [1947] 165 p.
   Reflections on the Golden Bed and other Stories. Bombay;
   Current Book House, n.d. 114 p.
   The first of these volumes contains nineteen stories and
   three prose poems; the second, fifteen stories including
   Lament on the Death of a Master of Arts; the third,
   twelve stories. A variety of characters in North Indian
   scenes.
   The Big Heart, A Novel. London, N.Y. [etc.] Hutchin-
   son International Authors [1945] 216 p.
   Deals with a community of coppersmiths in Amritsar,
   giving considerable information on their life and work.

Coolie. London, N.Y. [etc.]: Hutchinson International
Authors, 1947. 175 p.

The life of a coolie from the Punjab hills who works at
various jobs in North India and Bombay until his death
as a rickshawwallah in Simla.

Lament on the Death of a Master of Arts. Lucknow: Naya
Sansar [1939] 128 p.

The publisher's note on the cover says: "A boy
frustrated in his hopes of decent employment, dying in
agony of consumption . . . Perhaps the tale is an
offering on behalf of all our Indian youth, victims to
disease and the monstrous Moloch of government
service and social prestige . . ."

The Lost Child and Other Stories. [London] J. A. Allen,
1934.

Private Life of an Indian Prince, A Novel. London:
Hutchinson [1953] 346 p.

A diatribe against the princely order; the time is 1947,
the place, an imaginary princely state in Northern
India; sex and politics combine to land the prince finally
in an asylum for the insane.

Seven Summers; The Story of an Indian Childhood.
London, New York: Published for Hutchinson International Authors by Hutchinson, 1951. 238 p.

Autobiographical; memories of childhood in Western
Punjab in the period preceding 1914; author's father
served with a regiment at Nowshera; valuable for its
pictures of domestic life.

Two Leaves and a Bud. London: Lawrence and Wishart
[1937] 257, 13 p.

Lives of sahibs and coolies on a tea plantation in
Assam.

Untouchable, A Novel. With a preface by E. M. Forster. London, N.Y.: Hutchinson International Authors, 1947. 128 p.

A day in the life of a sweeper in a North Indian city.

The Village, A Novel by . . . London: J. Cape [1939] 351 p.

Across the Black Waters, A Novel by . . . London: J. Cape [1940] 11, 357, 13 p.

The Sword and the Sickle. A Novel by . . . London: J. Cape [1942] 9, 368 p.

These three novels form a trilogy; in the first, which offers a vivid, detailed picture of life in a Punjab village, the hero, a Sikh, eventually enlists in the Indian Army; in the second, he is a soldier in France during the first world war; in the third, he returns from war to find his family dead or scattered and his land lost, and he becomes involved in the peasant movement in the U.P.

ANAND, Mulk Raj and Iqbal Singh, eds. *Indian Short Stories*. London: The New India Publishing Co. [1946] 193 p.

Sixteen stories; in addition to the editors, contributors include, Rabindranath Tagore, Sarat Chandra Chatterji, Prem Chand, Raja Rao, Ahmed Ali, R. K. Narayan, Khwaja Ahmad Abbas, Tarashankar Bannerjee and others.

ATHAVALE, Mrs. Parvati, *My Story, The Autobiography of a Hindu Widow*. Written in the Marathi language. Translated by Rev. Justin E. Abbott. New York–London: G. E. Putnam's Sons. The Knickerbacker Press, 1930. xiv, 149 p.

Widowed at an early age, the author devoted her life to work for the Widow's Home in Poona established by her brother-in-law, Professor D. K. Karve; she relates at length her experiences in America, 1918–20.

BAHADUR, Umrao, *The Curse of Society*. [Delhi: Printing and Stationery Depot, n.d.] 121 p.
The "Curse" is the ban on marriage of widows; the widowed heroine does remarry but before this event occurs, the author takes advantage of the situation to describe in some detail the widow's lot.

Destiny. [Delhi: Printing and Stationery Depot, n.d.] 151 p. Romantic events in the life of a Muslim family of the upper class in North India.

The Unveiled Court: The Story of a Prince's Court. London: Arthur H. Stockwell, Ltd. [1932?] 94 p.
According to a statement in the *Cork Examiner*, reprinted in a copy of *The Curse of Society*, *The Unveiled Court* "describes, in vivid colours, the life of an imaginary Indian Prince . . . supplies a refreshing exposure of defects in the government under the regime of the Princely Order."

BALA KRISHNA MUDALIYAR, A, *The Reminiscences of a Retired Hindu Official, Containing Short Hints on Hindu Philosophy*. Madras: Commercial Press, 1905. ii, 142 p.

BANERJEA, S. B., *Indian Detective Stories*. London: Gay and Hancock [19—?] 275 p.

Tales of Bengal. Edited by Francis Henry Skrine, I.C.S. London: Longmans, Green, 1910. xxi, 187 p.
These seventeen sketches and stories of nineteenth century life in a Bengal village near Calcutta contain much information on values and attitudes, and on interpersonal relations.

I.F.I.E.–D

BANERJEE, Tarashankar, *Epoch's End*. Translated from Bengali, 'Manvantar' by Hirendranath Mookherjee. Calcutta: Mitralaya [1945] 314 p.

The Eternal Lotus. Translated from Bengali by Ela Sen. Calcutta: Purvasa Ltd., 1945.

BANERJEE, Upendra Nath, *Memoirs of a Revolutionary*. Calcutta: K. L. Chakravarty [1924 ?] ii, 174 p.

A member of the Yugantar group, author was sentenced for life to the Andamans, but released after World War I; much of the book is devoted to his prison experiences.

BANERJI, Nripendra Chandra, *At the Crossroads, 1885–1946; The Autobiography of* . . . Calcutta: A. Mukherjee, n.d. 318 p.

Nationalist and educationist, Banerji has written of his life as a student in Dacca and Calcutta, and as a college teacher; a large part of the book is devoted to reminiscences of political figures and developments during the first thirty years of the present century.

BANNERJEE, Manik, *Boatman of the Padma*. Translated from the Bengali by Hirendranath Mukerjee. Bombay: Kutub [1948] 187 p.

Good account of the life and work of some Bengal fishermen.

The Primeval and Other Stories. New Delhi: Peoples' Publishing House [1958] viii, 134 p.

"All about persons on the wrong side of the law", according to a review in the *Indian Review*, vol. 60, 1958.

BASU, Baren, *Rangrūt* (The Recruit). Translated from Bengali by Subrata Bannerji. Bombay: People's Publishing House, 1954. 272 p.

A Bengali in the army during the second world war. The publisher's note states that the novel "draws heavily on the author's army experience."

BASU, Subodh, *The City of New Moghuls*. Calcutta: [Published by Sailendra Chandra Bose 1947] 146 p.
Translated by the author from the Bengali *Rajdhani*. The city is New Delhi; the characters are for the most part transplanted Bengalis; the heroine is a student in a fashionable school for girls.

BHATTACHARYA, Bhabani, *He Who Rides a Tiger*. New York: Crown Publishers [1954] 245 p.
A Bengali blacksmith, caught up in the famine, produces a miracle, "becomes" a Brahman and proprietor of a temple.

Music for Mohini. New York: Crown Publishers [1952] 251 p.
A Bengali girl, brought up in a Calcutta family, with a modern education, is married to a man still living in his ancestral village home; major theme is the conflict between the traditional and the modern way of life; much ethnographic detail particularly with regard to marriage ceremonies and the first few days of a bride in her husband's home.

So Many Hungers! Bombay: Hind Kitabs [1947] 283 p.
Bengalis, rich and poor, city-dwellers and villagers, during the Second World War, and especially the famine.

BRINDA, Maharani of Kapurthala, *The Story of An Indian Princess*, as Told to Elaine Williams. New York: Henry Holt [1953] vii, 246 p.
The high life in India and Europe.

CHAKRAVARTI, Khetrapal, *Sarala and Hingana*, (*Tales Descriptive of Indian Life*). Calcutta: Basu, Mitra and Co. Printers and Publishers, 1895. 126 p.

CHAND, Prem (pseud. of Dhanpat Rai Srivastava), *Godan, A Novel of Peasant India*. Bombay: Jaico Publishing House [1957] 386 p.

The action takes place in a U.P. village and in Lucknow; the main characters are peasants, but moneylenders, zemindars, and members of business and professional classes also figure; the novel is valuable for the picture it gives of interpersonal relations within the family and the village and for its information on values and attitudes.

Short Stories of Prem Chand. Translated by Gurdial Mallik. Bombay: Nalanda Publications [1946] 166 p.

A Handful of Wheat. New Delhi: People's Publishing House, 1955. ix, 230 p.

The first volume contains eleven short stories; the second fifteen; several stories appear in both volumes. With a few exceptions these stories, and all the best of them, depict village life and people in Uttar Pradesh.

CHANDAR, Krishan, *Flame and the Flower*. With an introduction by Dr. Mulk Raj Anand. Bombay: Current Book House [1951] vii, 99 p.

These fifteen stories and sketches, written originally in Urdu, range in setting from Korea to Spain; one is a *Letter to a Dead Man*, addressed to an American soldier killed in Korea; one describes incidents on a train journey through Punjab during the 1947 riots; another is a story of Bombay millworkers; most of them express the writer's leftist point of view.

I cannot Die, A Story of Bengal. Translated from the original Urdu by Khwaja Ahmad Abbas. Poona: Kutub ⌈1943?⌉ 52 p.

The Bengal famine of 1942—as seen with the eyes of a member of a foreign consulate in Calcutta, an upper-class Bengali, and a victim.

CHANDU MENON, O., *Induleka: A Malayalam Novel.* Translated into English by W. Dumergue. Madras: Addison, 1890. xix, 304 p.

The principal characters of this novel, a love story, are Nayars and Nambudiris. While it is not intended as a completely realistic portrayal of contemporary society, the novel does present a picture of life in a joint Nayar family which is true to life in many respects; a chapter devoted to conversation on religion and politics reveals contemporary attitudes.

CHATTERJEE, Sita, *The Cage of Gold.* Translation by A. E. Brown. Calcutta: R. Chatterjee, 1923. 200 p.

This romantic tale contains some good pictures of domestic life in Calcutta.

The Knight Errant. Calcutta: Modern Review Office.

CHATTERJEE, Sita and Santa, *Tales of Bengal.* With an introduction by E. J. Thompson. London: H. Milford, Oxford University Press (An Eastern Library, no. 1) 1922. iv, 110 p.

Six short stories; excellent portraits of Bengali women; the traditional ideal woman appears in *Loyalty,* and others; a good deal of ethnography.

(Santa Devi and Seeta Devi), *The Garden Creeper.* Translated into English by Seeta Devi. Calcutta: R. Chatterjee ⌈Printed and Published by S. K. Das at the Prabasi Press 1931⌉ 332 p.

CHATTERJI, Bankim Chandra, *The Abbey of Bliss*. A Translation of Bankim Chandra Chatterjee's *Ānandamath*,
by Nares Chandra Sen-Gupta. Calcutta: Padmini
Mohan Neogi, n.d. xi. 201, vii p.

Dawn Over India. Translated and adapted from Bengali,
by Basanta Koomar Roy. New York: The Devin
Adair Co., 1941. 230 p.

The second of these two books is a version of *Ānandamath*, an historical novel of the Sanyasi rebellion in
Bengal about 1770, and Bankim Chandra's most famous
work. The "Abbey" makes it clear that the Sanyasis
were in revolt against Muslim rule (in North Bengal),
follows history in showing them at odds with the British
who were endeavouring to maintain law and order. In
the "Abbey", a rather mysterious "physician" appears
in the last chapter, who tells the Sanyasi leader that his
mission has been fulfilled: "The Mussalman rule has
come to an end"; and when the leader objects, saying,
"The English are still powerful at Calcutta", the
physician replies, "There is no hope of a revival of the
True Faith if the English be not our masters," and goes
on to expound Bankim Chandra's views of the need for
reforms. *Dawn Over India*, brought out at a critical
period in the Independence movement, omits all
reference to the Muslims, and depicts the Sanyasis in
revolt against the British; otherwise, it appears to
follow the original closely.

Chandra Shekhar, *A Bengali novel by the late Rai
Bahadoor* . . . translated by Manmatha Nath Ray
Chowdbury. London: Luzac and Co. n.d. [pref.
1904] viii, 317, vii p.

An historical novel of the eighteenth century; the lives
of various individuals, Hindu and Muslim, as well as

British, are depicted against the background of the war of the British against Mir Kassim Ali Khan.

Durgesa Nandini, or The Chieftain's Daughter. A Bengali Romance by . . . Translated into English prose by Charu Chandra Mookerjee. Calcutta: H. M. Mookerjee, 1880. ii, 204 p.

An historical novel of Bengal in the years of Akbar's reign; plot involves the attempt of Rajputs in the service of Akbar to conquer the last Pathan rulers of Bengal, but the novel is mainly a love story.

Indira and Other Stories. Translated by J. D. Anderson, with an introduction. Calcutta: The Modern Review Office, 1925. 148 p.

Contains, in addition to the title story, *Radharani, The Two Rings (Yugalāṅgurīya)*, and *Doctor Macrurus. Indira* is the story of a wife abducted on her way to her husband's home; she finally wins his love and forces him to receive her as his wife. In *Radharani*, a small girl is befriended by a stranger who turns up years later and marries her. *The Two Rings* has a complicated plot beginning with a horoscope and a prediction that the wife will cause her husband's death; a secret marriage follows at which husband and wife are blindfolded, and given two rings with which they are able to recognize each other later, and immediately separated. The locale is the ancient city of Tamluk in the pre-Muslim period. This story might have come directly out of the old Bengali metrical romances. *Doctor Macrurus* is a satire in which lions discuss the strange ways of men.

Kopal-Kundala: A Tale of Bengali Life. Translated from the Bengali of Bunkim Chandra Chatterjee by H. A. D. Phillips. London: Trübner, 1885. xxix, 208 p.

Although the scene is laid in Bengal in the time of Akbar, this is not primarily an historical novel; the tale, which has a tragic ending, depicts the hero involved with two women, one, his first wife, from whom he has become separated, and the second, brought up by a Kapalik, or Tantric worshipper, who plays the part of villain.

Krishna Kanta's Will. Translated by Miriam S. Knight with introduction, glossary and notes by J. F, Blumhardt. London: T. Fisher Unwin, 1895. 264 p.

A novel of life in nineteenth century Bengal; portrays a joint family with some detail; valuable for its information on values and attitudes and on interpersonal relations within the family. Blumhardt writes in his introduction: "the chief aim of the author in all his works appears to have been to promote the amelioration of Hindu society, and to teach the vital importance of a reliance on religious principles in the affairs of life."

The Poison Tree, *A Take of Hindu Life in Bengal*. Translated by Miriam S. Knight, with a preface by Edwin Arnold. London: T. Fisher Unwin, 1884. xiv, 318 p.

A translation of *Viṣavṛkṣa*. Excellent description of life in a zamindar's house in nineteenth century upcountry Bengal. Plot: Zamindar, already married, falls in love with beautiful young widowed member of the household; urged by his self-sacrificing wife, he marries the girl, following which his wife runs away from home; believed dead, she returns unexpectedly; by this time her husband realizes she is the one he loves, and the second wife takes poison and dies.

Rajani. Translated by P. Majumdar. Calcutta: The Book Company, n.d. iv, 206 p.

A romance with a beautiful blind flower-seller as heroine, and a complicated plot; scene laid for the most part in Calcutta.

Rajmohan's Wife. Calcutta: R. Chatterjee, 1935. iv, 155 p. This novel was written originally in English and serialized in the *Indian Field* (1864). A romantic tale of domestic life in an East Bengal village of the nineteenth century; the plot revolves around a much maltreated wife, her sister, and her sister's husband; the villains are all punished; the virtuous do not live happily ever after, but resign themselves to their fate.

Sitaram. An English translation of the Bengali novel by . . . [by] Sib Chandra Mukerji. Calcutta: R. Cambray, n.d. [pref. 1903] ii, 258 p.
An historical novel dealing with the rise and fall of an independent Hindu kingdom in seventeenth century Bengal.

Sree: An Episode from Bankim Chandra Chatterjee's novel "Sitaram", translated by P. N. Bose and H. W. B. Moreno. Calcutta: Printed and Published by H. W. B. Moreno at the Central Press, n.d. 38 p.

CHATTERJI, Sarat Chandra, *The Deliverance.* Translated from the original Bengali by Dilip Kumar Roy, revised by Sri Aurobindo, with a preface by Rabindranath Tagore. Bombay: N. M. Tripathi, Nalanda Publications. [1944] xvi, 104 p.
A translation of *Nishkriti.* Excellent description of a joint family in Bengal.

(Sarat Chandra) *The Eldest Sister and Other Stories.* Allahabad: Central Book Depot [1950] 125 p.
The first of these three stories is a translation of *Baṛādidī*, the love story of a Hindu widow; the second,

Vilāsi, "contains a bitter attack on conventional morality, being the story of the romance of a high caste Hindu and a snake-charmer's daughter." (S. C. Sen Gupta, p. 59); the third, a translation of *Chhabi*, is a love story with Burma in the pre-British period as its setting.

Srikanta, The Autobiography of a Wanderer. Translated by K. C. Sen and Theodosia Thompson, with an introduction by E. J. Thompson. London: Oxford University Press, 1922. xi, 175 p. Also, Benares: Indian Publishers [1945] iv, 154 p.

The Benares edition omits the introduction by Thompson; has an introduction by K. C. S. This book is the translation of the first part of a four-part novel. S. C. Sen Gupta (p. 80) says of the entire novel, that it is "partly a story of adventure, partly a travel diary, and partly a novel of love." K. C. S. in the introduction to the Benares edition writes that Srikanta is "generally understood to be largely autobiographical". The present volume relates a series of episodes in the life of the hero as a boy and young man in Bengal and Bihar.

CHATTOPADHYAYA, Harindranath, *Life and Myself*. Vol. I. Dawn Approaching Noon. Bombay: Nalanda Publications [1948] 222 p.

In part, a highly personal record; in part, sketches and reminiscences of certain members of the household and family, and other famous persons whom he met. This volume concludes with his return to India about 1921 after a couple of years spent in England, where he studied at Cambridge, and in Europe.

CHATTOPADHAYA, Romesh Chandra, *The Sorrows of a Sub-Postmaster: (A Story from Life)*. Calcutta: The Book Company [1927] 150 p.

CHAUDHURI, Nirad C., *The Autobiography of an Unknown Indian*. London: Macmillan, 1951. xii. 515 p.
Author was born in 1897, and his book contains much information on various aspects of life in the district of Mymensingh, East Bengal, in the early years of this century; it is invaluable for its pictures of life in Calcutta where the author lived from 1910–1942.

CHAUDHURI, Pramatha, *Tales of Four Friends*. Translated by Indira Devi Chaudhurani. [Published for Visva-Bharati by Pulinbihari Sen, 194?] 119 p.
A translation from the Bengali *Chār-iyārī-kathā*. Four romantic episodes involving Indian men and European women. A quotation from the *Times Literary Supplement* describes the book as "the Indian attempt to write the counterpart of such tales as Mr. Kipling's 'Without Benefit of Clergy' and Pierre Loti's romantic accounts of exotic amours."

CHETTUR, Govinda Krishna, *The Ghost City*. Mangalore: Basil Mission Bookshop [1932] iii, 227 p.
A collection of ten short stories.

CHETTUR, S. K., *Bombay Murder*. (Published about 1940). Srinivasa Iyengar (p. 205) says this is a "clever detective novel . . . which incidentally throws some light on the ultra-fashionable life lived by people in luxurious Bombay flats."

The Cobras of Dhermashevi and Other Stories. Madras and Bangalore: Higginbothams [1937] iv, 146 p.

Muffled Drums. (Published about 1927).

The Spell of Aphrodite and Other Stories. Bombay: Jaico Publishing House [1957] 192 p.

CHINNA DURAI, J., *"Sugirtha": An Indian Novel*. With a preface by the Hon. Gertrude Kinnaird. London: The Hulbert Publishing Co. [1929] i, 242 p.

According to Bhupal Singh (p. 308) this book is "instructive on the question of child marriages and the plight of widows—a book smacking of missionary propaganda."

CHINTAMANI, V. V., *Vedantam, the Clash of Traditions*. London: Heath Cranton [1938] 266 p.

Scene is laid in South India and England, where the hero is a student; the two traditions, Indian and English, are here proved irreconcilable.

CHITALE, Venu (pseud. of Mrs. Leelabai Khare), *In Transit*. Bombay: Hind Kitabs [1950] x, 504 p.

The chronicle of a Chitpavan Brahman family of Poona from 1915 to 1935, set against the background of political developments. The novel is essentially a picture, full of color and minute detail, of a way of life which seems likely to be gone forever.

DATTA, Dinescandra, *Matriculation Short Stories*. Jaipur City: Asian Publishing House [1948] 92 p.

DATTA, Sasi Chandra, *The Young Zemindar*. Three vols. [London] Remington, 1883.

DAY, Lal Behari, *Govinda Samanta, or, The History of a Bengal Raiyat*. London: Macmillan, 1874. viii, 383 p. Also published under the title, *Bengal Peasant Life*. London: Macmillan, 1908. xii, 383 p. (This edition contains three additional final chapters.)

This won a prize in 1871 offered for the best novel in Bengali or English illustrating the "Social and Domestic Life of the Rural Population and Working Classes of

Bengal"; much of it is pure ethnography. The scene is Burdwan District during the period 1850–1875.

DAY, Rash Behari, *My Days with Uncle Sam*. [Printed by S. A. Gunny, Alexander S. M. Press, Dacca], 1919. iv, 289 p.
Stimulated by his reading of Swami Vivekananda, author determined to go to the U.S.A.; made his way to Bombay where he got a job as a sailor on a boat to Calcutta, thence to New York; spent seven years working at various jobs and studying electrical engineering at Tuskegee Institute before returning to India; his book is full of observations of American society as contrasted with his own.

DE, R. P., *Mother and Daughter, or, A True Picture of Hindu Life of Bengal*. Calcutta: Oriental Publishing Co. [Printed and Published by D. N. Bose. n.d.] 185 p.
Trials and tribulations of a poor Brahman widow and her daughter in a Bengal village of the nineteenth century; contains some information on manners and customs.

DEOBHANKAR, N. R., *Hemakumari and Other Stories*. Foreword by Sarojini Naidu. Bombay: Nalanda Publications, 1949. 200 p.
The emphasis of these seventeen stories is on plot; humor and pathos are both represented.

DUTT, Ajoy C., *Reminiscences*. Bombay: Padma Publishers. (1949?)

DUTT, H., *Bijoy Chand: An Indian Tale*. Calcutta: H. C. Dutt, 1888, 29 p.

Lieut. Suresh Biswas: His Life and Adventures. Calcutta: P. C. Dass [1900] viii, 171 p.

DUTT, Romesh Chander, *The Lake of Palms; A Story of*
  Indian Domestic Life. Translated into English by
  Romesh Dutt. London: T. F. Unwin, 1902. viii, 256 p.
Pictures life in a Bengal village and in Calcutta in the
late nineteenth century; excellent description of a
pilgrimage to Puri; one of the themes is the question of
widow-marriage.

Pratap Singh, The Last of the Rajputs (A Tale of Rajput
  Courage and Chivalry). Rendered into English by Ajoy
  C. Dutt. Allahabad: Kitabistan [1943] viii, 183 p.
A translation of *Rājput Jivan-sandhyā*; set against the
background of Akbar's struggle to conquer Mewar is
the story of a feud between members of two rival
Rajput clans.

Sivaji, A Historical Tale of the Great Mahratta Hero and
  Patriot. Rendered into English by Ajoy C. Dutt.
  Allahabad: Kitabistan [1944] vii, 264 p.
This is a translation of *Mahārāshtra Jivan-prabhāt.*
Mingled with an account of Sivaji's life and exploits
from about 1665 to 1667 is the love story of a Rajput
in his service.

The Slave Girl of Agra, an Indian Historical Romance.
  London: T. Fisher Unwin, 1909. viii, 9–316 p.
This is a translation by the author of his Bengali novel,
Mādhavi Kaṅkan. According to Srinivasa Iyengar (p.
169) it "deals with Mughal times and gives a picture of
social life in the sixteenth and seventeenth centuries."

Todar Mull, the Conqueror of Bengal, an Historical Novel.
  Rendered into English from Vanga Vijeta by Ajoy
  Dutt. Allahabad: Kitabistan [1947] 165 p.
Todar Mull is the famous minister of Akbar; the novel
is a romance of sixteenth century Bengal and the Hindu
zamindars.

DUTT, S., *Stories from Bengal, compiled by* . . . Bombay: Jaico Publishing House [1957] 190 p.

Nine stories translated from Bengali by S. Dutt; authors represented are: Rabindranath Tagore; Sarat Chandra Chatterjee, Pramatha Chowdhury, Prabodh Kumar Sanyal, Premendra Mitra, Hari Narayan Chattopadhyaya, Santosh Kumar Ghose, Tara Shankar Bandyopadhyaya, Achintya Kumar Sen-Gupta. Two of these stories appear in Lila Ray's collection, *Broken Bread*.

DUTT, Ullaskar, *Twelve Years of My Prison Life*. Calcutta: The Arya Publishing House [1924] iv, 292 p.

Tried and convicted in the Alipore Bomb Case, Dutt, after a short stay in the Andamans, was committed to the Government Lunatic Asylum in Madras where he remained until his release. B. Burman, who translated the book from the original Bengali says the "main theme of this Vol. is the extraordinary spiritual experiences of the author during his incarceration."

FUTEHALLY, Zeenuth, *Zohra*. Bombay: Hind Kitabs [1951] 325 p.

Domestic life of upper class Muslim families in Hyderabad about 1930 portrayed with a wealth of detail.

GANDHI, Prabhudas, *My Childhood with Gandhiji*. Ahmedabad: Navajivan Publishing House [1957] xvi, 212 p.

GANGULI, Taraknath, *Svarnalata. A Glimpse into the Indian Inner Home, being a faithful rendering into English of the late Babu Taraknath Ganguli's popular Bengali novel, Svarnalata, by Bidhubhushan Mukerjee*. Calcutta: S. K. Lahiri, 1903. viii, 301 p.

Bidhubhushan Mukerjee in his preface writes: "The Bengali as he is—the Bengali with all his virtues and all his vices—is faithfully depicted in these pages . . ." J. C. Ghosh writes (p. 166) of the book that "it still retains its interest as the most realistic picture of middle-class life in our literature." Edward Thompson in his own novel, *An Indian Day*, refers to this as "that most charming of Bengali novels."

The Brothers, from the Bengali of Svarnalata, a Novel by Taraknath Ganguli; translated by Edward Thompson. London: The India Society, 1928. 181 p.

A substantial part of the original, a romantic love episode, is omitted in this translation.

Mrs. GHOSAL (Srimati Svarna Kumari Devi), *The Fatal Garland*. New York: Macmillan, n.d. 224 p.

An historical romance of fifteenth century Bengal.

Short Stories. Madras: Ganesh, n.d. iii, 242 p.

These fourteen stories, a couple of which have an historical background, throw light on family life in Bengal.

An Unfinished Song. New York: Macmillan [1913] 219 p. Another edition is given the title: *To Whom? An Indian Love-Story*. Translated from the original Bengali by Sovona Devi. Calcutta: S. K. Lahiri [pref. 1910] 207 p.

The novel is a love story; the characters are Westernized Bengalis.

GHOSE, Barindra Kumar, *The Tale of My Exile*. Pondicherry: Arya Office, 1922. 168 p.

Author was convicted in Alipore Bomb Case, sentenced to the Andamans in 1909, released about 1920; his book is a rather impersonal record of prison experiences.

GHOSE, Sudhin N., *And Gazelles Leaping*. New York: Macmillan, 1949. 238 p.

> *Cradle of the Clouds*. New York: Macmillan, 1951. 304 p.

> *The Vermillion Boat*. New York: Macmillan, 1953. 302 p.

> *The Flame of the Forest*. New York: Macmillan, 1955. 288 p.

These four novels are based on the author's life in a West Bengal village and Calcutta; together they form a sophisticated autobiography not designed to give a realistic portrayal of people and events.

GHOSH, Sarath Kumar, *The Prince of Destiny, the New Krishna*. London: Rebman, 1909. viii, 630 p.

The Prince is a Rajput ruler of a princely state in the last years of the nineteenth century. Having absorbed the best of both East and West, he rejects his "destiny" to lead a revolution against the British, and adopts the life of a holy man in order to preach the doctrine of peace. In this highly romantic novel a number of the main characters are British. The novel is addressed primarily to the British, and, according to the publisher's preface, it "reveals the Indian view of the causes of the present unrest, and Britain's unseen peril in India."

> *Verdict of the Gods*. New York: Dodd, Mead, 1905. 307 p. Also published under the title of: 1001 *Indian Nights (The Trials of Narayan Lal)*. London: William Heinemann, 1906. 247 p.

A kind of fairy tale; the Prince, after numerous ordeals, wins the Princess.

I.F.I.E.—E

GOKHALE, Aravind, *The Unmarried Widow and Other Stories*. Translated from Marathi by Smt. Sneh-prabha Pradhan. Bombay: Jaico Publishing House [1957] 121 p.

Women from various walks of life, and in various roles, figure in these twelve stories; several are love stories.

GOPAL, Ram, *Rhythm in the Heavens, An Autobiography*. London: Secker and Warburg, 1957. xii. 212 p.

The dancer writes mostly about his life as a performer, a little about his early years and training.

GOUR, Sir Hari Singh, *His Only Love*. London: Henry Walker [1930] 7, 288 p.

Bhupal Singh (p. 309): "He takes us to a world that is neither Eastern nor Western."
Lost Souls, A Story of the Indian Revolution.

GUPTA, Dilip K., ed., *Best Stories of Modern Bengal*. Translated by Nilima Devi, Two Vols. Calcutta: The Signet Press [1944, 1945] 332 p., 358 p.

Vol. I contains twelve stories; vol. II, fourteen; most of these depict domestic life in Bengal; authors repre-sented are: Manik Banerjee, Buddhadeva Bose, Pre-mendra Mitra, Subodh Ghose, Achintya Kumar Sen Gupta, Ananda Sankar Roy, and others.

GUPTA, Nagendranath, *Reflections and Reminiscences*. Bombay: Hind Kitabs [1947] 220 p.

Gupta (1862–1940), a Bengali man of letters, born in Bihar, was for some time a newspaper editor in Karachi and Lahore. His book is largely concerned with pro-minent individuals, mostly Indian, in Bengal, Sind, and Punjab, whom he knew; it affords a few glimpses of social life in these provinces.

GURU, Kumara (pseud. of C. Subramania Ayyar), *Life's Shadows*. Vol. I. Foreword by Sir S. Radhakrishnan. Bombay: Tareporevala Sons [1938] 166 p.

Life's Shadows, A Daughter's Shadow. Vol. II. Madras: Published by C. Subramania Ayyar [1943] 38 p.

In the preface to Vol. I, the author states that his aim "has been to present, from a psychical standpoint and in various aspects, a realistic picture of the educated Tamil Brahmin of the last generation." Four sketches treat the relations of a man with his brother, wife, son, and friend; Vol. II contains a fifth sketch which treats relations between a man and his daughters. Radhakrishnan writes in the foreword: "These stories of India in transition are a mild protest against the Westernization of the soul of India, that is now in process."

HABIB, Muhammad, *The Desecrated Bones and Other Stories*. Oxford University Press, 1925. 185 p.

Three stories with a setting in the U.P.; one is contemporary; one, six hundred years ago; one, in the time of Akbar.

HAZARI, *An Indian Outcaste. The Autobiography of an Untouchable*. London: Bannisdale Press [1951] 151 p.

Born in Moradabad District in the U.P., this member of an untouchable caste worked as a servant in various European families and hotels in North India Hill Stations, Delhi, Bombay, Aligarh; finally became a Muslim, acquired an education, and at the book's end, goes to Europe to study as a protégé of a British teacher at Aligarh. His account of his life contains some information on family life and the customs of his caste, also intercaste relations.

HOME, D. C., *Floods along the Ganges*. Bombay: Peoples'
Publishing House [1953] 152 p.

Deals with the growth of political consciousness among
peasants in Bengal during the first half of the present
century; ends with partition.

Poison and Passion. Bombay: Kanak Publishers [1955]
245 p. Movie stars at work and at play, in Bombay.

So Many! So Gallant! Bombay: Current Book House
[1951] 106 p.

Bombay in the 'thirties; characters are students and
workers of various sorts with interests in Marxism.

HOSAIN, Attia, *Phoenix Fled and Other Stories*. London:
Chatto and Windus, 1953. 202 p.

Twelve stories; most of them portray Muslim women
of North India.

HUSSAIN, Iqbalunnisa, *Purdah and Polygamy, Life in an
Indian Muslim Household*. Bangalore: Printed by
D. N. Hosali, at the Hosali Press, 1944. 4, 309 p.

Sir Ramalinga Reddy in a foreword characterizes the
author as the "Jane Austen of India". The main characters belong to the mercantile class of the Muslim
community; the exact locale of the story is not specified;
considerable ethnography.

HUTHEESING, Krishna, *Shadows on the Wall*. New York:
John Day [1948] vi, 116 p.

Twelve stories of Indian women, "fellow prisoners,
politicals and convicts who were with . . . [the author]
. . . . in jail many years ago". (Pref.)

With No Regrets, An Autobiography. New York: John
Day [1945] 160 p.

For the most part devoted to recollections of the
members of her famous family.

Isvani, *Girl in Bombay*. London: Pilot Press, 1947. v,
    199 p. Also published under the title, *The Brocaded
    Sari*. New York: John Day [1946] 205 p.

The author says in a foreword: "It is many years since
I have seen the land of my birth . . . But I will try to be
as accurate as possible in setting down my memories, as
well as what was told me as a child." A member of the
Khoja Muslim community, she writes of her girlhood,
her marriage about 1921 which ended in divorce a few
years later, and finally of her departure for England to
continue her studies.

Isvaran, Manjeri S., *Angry Dust*. Madras: Shakti
    Karyalayam [1944] 120 p.

No Anklet Bells for Her. (*Stories*) With an introduction
    by John Hampson. Madras: Mitra [1949] xvi,
    155 p.

Painted Tigers, Stories. Madras: Dhanus, 1956. 134 p.

Rickshawallah, Short Stories. Madras: The Alliance Co.,
    1946. xiii, 126 p.

Many of these stories of South India are valuable for
their information on interpersonal relations; several
explore various aspects of the relationship between
husband and wife. Isvaran occasionally makes effective
use of the supernatural, though most of his stories are
realistic. *Rickshawallah* contains a short, prefatory note,
Something of Others and—Myself, in which the author
discusses the short story, Russian, English, and Indian.
The first of these collections contains nine stories; the
second, twelve; the third, nine; and the fourth, ten. One
of the stories in *No Anklet Bells for Her* was written
originally in Tamil by T. J. Ranganathan, and translated
by Isvaran.

Fancy Tales. Madras: Shakti Karyalayam, 1947. 64 p.
Fourteen once-upon-a-time stories of gods and god-
desses, kings and queens, apes, buffaloes, birds, etc.

Immersion, A Story. Madras: S. Viswanathan [1951]
78 p.
A man and his wife journey to Benares with his father's
ashes; on the way the woman allows herself to be
seduced; the story reaches a climax with her revenge.

Naked Shingles. (Published in 1941).

Siva Ratri.

KABIR, Humayan, *Men and Rivers.* Bombay: Hind Kitabs
[1947] 183 p.
The river is the Padma; the men are Muslim peasants.
Three Stories. Bombay: Hind Kitabs [1947] 80 p.
Written in the 'thirties, these stories deal with aspects
of contemporary Indian Muslim life.

KABIR, Humayun, ed.; Tarasankar Banerjee, Premendra
Mitra, associated eds., *Green and Gold, Stories and
Poems from Bengal.* Bombay [etc.]: Asia Publishing
House [1957] xi, 283 p.
Fifteen modern short story writers are represented in
this collection.

KAPUR, Pushpa, *Rajni.* New Delhi: Ramakrishna and Sons
[19—] 265 p.
Deals essentially with the problems of life and especially
of marriage which sophisticated, educated Indians face
today. The characters are Punjabis, the period is the
second World War.

KAPUR, Vimla, *Life Goes On.* Lahore: Associated Publications, 1946. 274 p.

KARAKA, D. F., *Just Flesh*. Bombay: Thacker [1941]
312 p.
The place, London and Oxford; the time, the 'thirties;
the characters, English.
There Lay the City. Bombay: Thacker, 1944. 269 p.
Bombay during the second world war is the scene of this
love story; the characters are Indians and Anglo-
Indians.

KARANTH, K. S., *Back to the Soul*. Translated by A. N.
Murthy Rao. Puttur, S. K.: Harsha Printery and
Publications, 1950. ii, 368 p.
Excellent descriptions of village life and people along
the West coast, in the Kanada area; considerable
ethnography.

KAUL, Narendranath, *The Heart's Way*. New Delhi:
Hamsa [1957] 156 p.
In a long letter, written to a woman shortly after her
marriage, a young man reviews the story of his hopeless
love for her, expounds his ideas on life, sex, marriage,
etc.

KAVERI Bai, Miss H., *Meenakshi's Memoirs*. Madras: G. A.
Natesan, 1937. xiv, 572 p.

KHAN, Nawab Bahadur Abdul Latif, *A Short Account of My
Public Life*. Calcutta: Newman and Co., 1885. 44 p.

KRISHNA, Bal, *The Love of Kusuma, An Eastern Love Story*.
London: T. Werner Laurie [1910] 236 p.
Srinivasa Iyengar (p. 177) says this is an attempt "to
delineate the minutiae of Indian social life."

KUMAR, Jainendra, *The Resignation, A Novel*. Translated
into English and edited by S. H. Vatsyayan. Delhi:
Siddhartha Publications, n.d. vi, 106 p.

This is a translation of the Hindi novel *Tyāgapatra* first published in 1937. It depicts the life of a "fallen" woman. The translator writes in a foreword: "Throughout the book it is the question of her *dharma* that confronts her . . . Jainendra Kumar is deeply concerned with the potentialities of non-resistence to evil as a positive spiritual force."

LAHIRI, Kali Krishna, *Roshinara, A Historical Romance, from the Bengali of . . . by (the late) Nobo Chandra Sen.* Trichinopoly: The Wednesday Review Press, 1912. iii, 275, iii p.

First published in Bengali in 1869, this must be one of the first novels with Sivaji as the hero; Roshinara, the heroine, is the daughter of Aurangzeb.

LALL, Anand, *The House at Adampur, a Story of Modern India.* New York: Knopf, 1956, 245 p.

The story of a wealthy Hindu, his family and friends in and around Delhi during the years 1930–44; contrasts the old and the new in Indian life; political developments of the time are given some prominence.

Seasons of Jupiter, A Novel of India. New York: Harper [1958] 253 p.

The hero, member of a wealthy, upper class family of Amritsar, tells the story of his experiences during a life-long search for a fully satisfying way of life.

MADHAVIAH, A., *Clarinda: A Historical Novel.* Tondiarpet [Madras]: Printed at the Cambridge Press, 1915. 258 p.

According to a review in the *Modern Review*, Vol. XIX, April, 1916, Clarinda was an historical character, the widow of a Mahratta Brahman who had been in the service of the ruler of Tanjore; she later became the concubine of an English officer who instructed her in Christian doctrine, and after his death she was baptized at Palamcottah where she later built the first Christian Church in that part of the country.

Kusika's Short Stories (on Marriage Reform and Allied Topics) First Part—Fifteen Stories, Second Part, Twelve Stories. Madras: The Author's Press and Publishing House, 1924. 124, and 128 p.

There was an earlier edition: *Short Stories*, by "*Kusika*" and *Short Stories (Second Series) by "Kusika"*. This edition of the second series was published in Madras, by the Methodist Publishing House in 1916, and has a foreword by S. Kasturi Ranga Iyengar. It contains sixteen short stories; all point the need for social reform, in regard to the dowry system, untouchability, etc. They give a picture, "true to life in the main incidents", according to Ranga Iyengar in the introduction, of "conditions obtaining chiefly among the . . . higher castes in Southern India".

Lieut. Panju, A Modern Indian. Madras: The Author's Press and Publishing House, 1924. 210 p.

Muthumeenakshi: The Autobiography of a Brahmin Girl. Translated from Tamil by one of his daughters. With an introduction by Sir C. Sankaran Nair. Madras: Law Printing House, 1915. 121 p.

According to a review in the *Modern Review*, Vol. XIX, April, 1916, the heroine is a girl whose "sad and sorrowful life was typical of the lives of thousands of girls in our country . . . describes the cruelty of the step-mother, the tyranny of the mother-in-law, and the misfortunes of the wretched widow."

Thillai Govindan. With an introduction by Frederic Harrison. London: T. Fisher Unwin [1916] xv, 174 p.

Professes to be the memoirs of a South Indian Brahman, brought up in a village, and given a university education, who finally, after a career as a government servant, reaffirms his faith in Indian values; valuable for its vignettes of village life, and its information on Brahman attitudes and values. Srinivasa Iyengar says, "perhaps the book is slightly autobiographical." (p. 173)

MARKANDAYA, Kamala (pseud. of Kamala [Purnaiya] Taylor), *Nectar in a Sieve.* New York: John Day [1954] 256 p.

Peasant life in South India; purports to be recollections of a village woman, told in the first person.

Some Inner Fury. New York: John Day [1956] 255 p.

The love story of an Indian girl and an Englishman comes to an end in 1942; a minor theme is the conflict between modern and orthodox Indians.

MEHTA, Perin C., *Short Stories.* [Bombay: Printed and Published by P. S. Jhabvala at Asian Printers, n.d.] 55 p.

Ten short stories of modern India. Author writes in introduction, "Today in an awakened India governed on modern lines . . . Sitas and Savitris yet prevail."

MEHTA, Ved, *Face to Face, An Autobiography.* Boston: Little, Brown, 1957. 370 p.

The author, blind from the age of three years, writes in his foreword, ". . . . the narrative is a succession of images, images collected from old and new India—one eclipsed, one rising—and from America . . ." The first two-thirds of the book deal with his life at a school for the blind in Bombay, at home with his family, and his experiences during Partition; the final section is an account of his life as a student in the United States.

MIRZA, Naderbeg K., *Dilkusha: A Romance of Sind Life*. Karachi: Sind Publishing House [1925] 228, iii p.

MITRA, J. N., *Towards the Dawn, A Political Novel of India's New Life*. Lucknow: K. C. Banerjee at the Anglo-Oriental Press, 1922. 251 p.

MITRA, Piari Chand (Tek Chand Thakur), *The Spoilt Child, A Tale of Hindu Domestic Life*. Translated from Bengali by G. D. Oswell. Calcutta: Thacker, Spink, n.d. xiv, 234 p.
This is a translation of *Ālāler Gharer Dulāl*. A good deal of Bengali life of the middle nineteenth century has been transferred to these pages; the translator in his preface writes: "Some of the reigning vices and follies of the time are held up to scorn"; many discursive passages clearly set forth what may be considered attitudes of a typical orthodox Hindu of the period.

MITRA, Premendra, *Kaleidoscope, A Novel*. Translated from the Bengali 'Michil' by Ela Sen. Calcutta: Purvasa [1945] 116 p.

MITRA, S. M., *Hindupore, A Peep behind the Indian Unrest. An Anglo-Indian Romance*. London: Luzac, 1909. viii, 317 p.
In his preface the author says, "My articles on the Indian Unrest in the *Nineteenth Century* were well received, and I was asked to deal with the subject in a more popular form. That is the genesis of 'Hindupore' ". The novel, which culminates in the marriage of an Irish lord to a Rajput princess, is an effort to explain India

and Indians to the British, and a plea for sympathy; it is
one of the few novels on this list in which Britishers are
among the major characters.

MUKHERJI, Probhat Chandra, *Stories of Bengali Life*.
Translated by Miriam S. Knight and the author.
Calcutta: Chuckervertty, Chatterji, 1912. 256 p.

NAGARAJAN, K., *Athawar House*. Madras and Bangalore:
Higginbothams [1937?] 312 p.
According to Srinivasa Iyengar (p. 202) this novel gives
an "enduring picture of a Maratha Brahmin family living
in South India."
Cold Rice. Madras: Shakti Karyalayam [1945] 163 p.
A dozen short stories; author states in a note that "the
locale is largely the Coromandel coast"; the time is the
period between the two world wars; educated towns-
people, officials, villagers, and a few Europeans people
Nagarajan's world.

NANDA, Savitri Devi, *The City of Two Gateways, The Autobiography of an Indian Girl*. London: Allen and
Unwin [1950] 278 p.
Story of the author's childhood and youth in Punjab;
much material on family life.

NARAIN, Ram, *The Tigress of the Harem*. New York:
Macaulay [1930]. 388 p. Sensational goings-on in a
princely state.

NARAYAN, R. K., *The Batchelor of Arts, A Novel by* . . .
With an introduction by Graham Greene. London,
New York [etc.]: T. Nelson [1937] x, 11–265 p.
Depicts the hero during the latter part of his college
career and, as he continues his education more in-
formally, for a few years thereafter.

The Dark Room: A Novel. London: Macmillan, 1938. 209 p.

A domestic tragi-comedy involving principally wife, husband and a second woman; the dark room is a store room to which the aggrieved wife retires.

The English Teacher. London: Eyre and Spottiswoode [1945] 183 p. Published under title, *Grateful to Life and Death.* [East Lansing) Michigan State College Press, 1953. 213 p.

The hero is a teacher of English but the novel is concerned primarily with his domestic and personal life as son, father, and husband.

The Financial Expert, A novel. With an introduction by Graham Greene. London: Methuen [1952] 217 p.

Triumphs and vicissitudes in the private and public life of a money-lender.

The Guide, A novel by . . . New York: The Viking Press, 1958. 220 p.

Traces the career of Raju—from shopkeeper to tourist guide—to impresario—to holy man.

Mr. Sampath. London: Eyre and Spottiswoode [1949]. 219 p. Published under title, *The Printer of Malgudi,* East Lansing: Michigan State University Press, 1957. 276 p.

An idealistic editor and an eccentric printer become involved with a film company and the production of a movie.

Swami and Friends. Mysore: Indian Thought Publications [1944] 197 p.

Episodes in the life of a small boy, at home, at school, at play.

Waiting for the Mahatma. London: Methuen [1955] 256 p.

An innocent falls in love and is caught up in the Quit India movement.

An Astrologer's Day, and Other Stories. London: Eyre and Spottiswoode, 1947. vi, 229 p.

Cyclone and Other Stories. Mysore: Indian Thought Publications, n.d. 120 p.

Dodu and Other Stories. Mysore: Indian Thought Publications, n.d. 145 p.

Lawley Road (Thirty-two Short Stories). Mysore: Indian Thought Publications [1956] 163 p.

Malgudi Days (Short Stories). Mysore: Indian Thought Publications, 1943. 119 p.

Many of the stories in these volumes add to the picture of Malgudi and its people, the world Narayan has brought to life in his novels. The Madras *Hindu*, where many of his stories first appeared, writes of Narayan: "He is one of the very few writers of fiction who does not falsify his picture of Indian society in order to excite false pathos or point a moral." The first of these volumes contains thirty stories; the second, eighteen; the third, seventeen; the fifth, nineteen.

NAYAR, Unni, *My Malabar.* Bombay: Hind Kitabs [1952] 136 p.

The first part of this book is autobiographical, based on memories of childhood in a joint family; the second consists of twelve sketches of individuals, and short tales; the author's intention was "to let those who have never been there see something of the people of Malabar."

NIKAMBÉ, Shevantibai M., *Ratanbai: A Sketch of a Bombay High Caste Hindu Young Wife*. With a preface by The Lady Harris. London: Marshall Brothers, 1895. viii, 88 p.

This little book, slight as to plot, is full of incidents which throw light on family life, interpersonal relations, values and attitudes among Maratha Brahmans.

NOON, Firoz Khan, *Scented Dust*. Lahore: R. S. M. Gulab Singh, 1942. 494 p.

In the foreword the author writes that he met an American lady who was "particularly interested to know of the life in the villages, the economic position of the peasantry, our system of taxation, the condition of our women, our religions, our politics, what it was that prevented the people in joining hands against the British, our system of Government, the place in it of the British officer, how he behaved towards the people, and what was the constitutional future of India. She was not willing to read any book written by a European no matter how objective." The author attempted to "answer her queries" with this novel.

PADMANABHA Iyer, P., *Indian Tales*. Srirangam: Sri Vani Vilas Press, 1924. 65 p.

PAL, Bipin Chandra, *Memories of My Life and Times*. Vol. I *In the Days of My Youth* (1857–1884). Calcutta: Modern Book Agency, 1932. xiv, 465 p.; Vol. II (1886–1900). Calcutta: Yugayatri Prakashak, 1951. vii, lxi, 296 p.

Vol. I is of great value for its glimpses of life in an eastern Bengal village and in Sylhet; for its account of student life in Calcutta; for its information on the

Brahmo Samaj, and various other aspects of the Bengal renaissance. In Vol. II, Pal takes up the story of his public life as a journalist and nationalist, but devotes considerable space to his spiritual development; the final chapters deal with his visit to England and America.

PANCHAPAKESA AYYAR, A. S., *Baladitya, A Historical Romance of Ancient India.* Bombay: Taraporevala Sons, 1930. xii, 402 p.

A novel of the Gupta period: the author writes in the introduction: "I have been more particular in representing what I consider to be the true spirit of the age rather than in sticking to historical facts even in details."

The Finger of Destiny and Other Stories. Kumbakonam: G. V. K. Swamy [1932] 180 p.

Indian After-dinner Stories. Bombay: D. B. Taraporewala Sons [1928] x, 135 p.

One hundred and twenty very short pieces to point a moral; first thirty-three are old stories "retouched and retold", pertaining to the lives of Buddha, Mahavira, Sankaracharya, etc.

An Indian in Western Europe. Bangalore: R. C. S. Maniam [1929–30] 2 Vols. iii, 400 p.

Author went to England in 1919 to study for the I.C.S. examination; here records his impressions of England and Europe.

Sense in Sex and Other Stories of Indian Women. Bombay: D. B. Taraporewala Sons, 1929. 288 p.

Author says in preface that "these stories are true to Indian life, especially of the South" and that the characters and incidents are "such as can be easily met with in real life." Twelve stories.

Three Men of Destiny. Madras: C. Coomarasawmy Naidu, 1939. xxix, 407 p.

The three are Alexander, Chandragupta Maurya, and Chanakya.

PANDIT, Vijaya Lakshmi, *Prison Days*. Calcutta: The Signet Press, 1946. 111 p.

Pages from a diary kept from August, 1942–June, 1943, while author was in Naini Tal jail as a political prisoner.

PARMANAND, Bhai, *The Story of My Life*. Translated from Hindi by N. Sundara Iyer. Madras: S. Ganesan [1923?] xv, 183 p.

According to a review in the *Modern Review*, Vol. XXXV, May, 1924, p. 596, this is an "account of his early life, travels, imprisonment in the Andamans, and in short, all his pain and sufferings in the cause of the country."

PHADKE, N. S., *Leaves in the August Wind, A Novel with the Indian Upheaval of August 1942 for its Background*. Bombay: Hind Kitabs [1947] 24, 174 p.

Scene is laid in Kolhapur State. First published in Marathi in 1943, the book was proscribed in 1944 by the Government of Bombay and in all Maratha States. The book contains an interesting prefatory statement concerning the defense of the novel by the author in an endeavour to have the ban lifted. His council agreed that the "essential theme of the book was the study of the psychology of a woman who finds herself inextricably involved in the lives of two men, Balasaheb, to whom she is married but whom she does not love, and with whose ideologies she is in complete conflict, and the other . . . whom she loves but to whom she is not married, and whose ideas are in complete harmony with her's." Novel on one level is an interesting attempt to dramatize the ideological conflict between the Indian National Congress and the Hindu Mahasabha.

The Whirlwind (*Jhanjavat*). Bombay [etc.]: Jaico Publishing House [1956] 187 p.

Originally written in Marathi, this is a story of the 1942 Quit India movement in Maharashtra.

PRASAD, Rajendra, *Autobiography*. Bombay [etc.]: Asia Publishing House [1957] x, 624 p.

Written largely in jail, in the years between 1942–45, this is for the most part the story of the author's public life and activities up to 1946.

RAJAGOPALACHARI, C., *The Fatal Cart and Other Stories*. New Delhi: The Hindustan Times [1946?] 140 p.

Sixteen stories translated from the Tamil by the author's son; varied scenes and characters in present-day South India.

RAJAM AIYAR, B. R., *True Greatness or Vasudeva Sastri*. Published in his *Rambles in Vedanta*, Being a Collection of His Contributions to the *Prabuddha Bharata*, 1896–98. London: George Allen and Unwin [1925] xxxix, 888 p. [The novel, pp. 619–734.]

"Reader! this is a religious novel . . ." (p. 636) Scene is Tamiland in the late nineteenth century. The novel was not completed.

RAJAN, Balachandra, *The Dark Dancer*. New York: Simon and Schuster, 1958. 308 p.

The hero, "England-returned", finds himself as a result of private and public upheavals during 1947.

RAM, Shankar (pseud. of T. L. Natesan), *The Children of the Kaveri*. Madras: A. N. Purnah, 1941. 98 p.

Creatures All. Madras: A. N. Purnah, 1933. 113 p.
These two volumes of short stories, containing five in
the first, six in the second collection, depict various
aspects of life in South India.

The Love of Dust. Madras. A. N. Purnah, 1938. 278 p.
Peasants along the Cauvery; of interest especially for its
descriptions of family life.

RAMABHADRAN, N., *Kettle Drums.* With a foreword by
R. S. Sarma. Mangalore, S. K.: Printed at the Basil
Mission Press, 1933. viii, 161 p.
A miscellany of nineteen stories, sketches and articles on
various subjects, some apparently written out of the
author's experience as a member of the police force; of
special interest for ethnographers are the sketches of the
village headman, accountant, schoolmaster, and land-
lord.

RAMACHANDRA RAO, D. S., *Lakshmi's Triumph: A Message
from the Stars.* Madras: G. A. Natesan [1936] 212 p.

RAMAKRISHNAN, T., *Early Reminiscences of . . . by Himself.*
Printed for Private Circulation Only. [Madras] 1907.
98, 15 p.
The reminiscences largely pertain to the author's school
and college life, at a mission school in Conjeevaram, at
Madras Christian College, and Madras University; to
which are added rather impersonal reflections on aspects
of Hindu social life and religion.

The Dive for Death: An Indian Romance. London:
George Allen, 1911. 153 p.
Srinivasa Iyengar (p. 173) writes of this novel, that it is
"based on certain South Indian superstitions and has
on the whole an eerie atmosphere."

I.F.I.E.–F*

Padmini: An Indian Romance. With an introduction by
the Right Hon. James Bryce. London: Swan Sonnen-
schein, 1903. viii, 214 p.

An historical novel, primarily a love story, of the
seventeenth century following the fall of the Vijayanagar
empire. It ends with the establishment of the British in
Madras.

RAMA RAO, Santha, *Home to India.* New York: Harper
[1945] 236 p.

In 1936 the author returned to India at the age of
sixteen after a ten-year absence during which she was
educated in England; she records her impressions before
she leaves for the United States in 1941.

Remember the House. New York: Harper, 1956. 241 p.

Life in Bombay City as lived by the Westernized, up-
rooted, pseudo-sophisticated set, contrasted with life in
Malabar based on traditional values.

RANADE, Ramabai, *Himself, the Autobiography of a Hindu
Lady.* Translated and adapted by Katherine Van Akin
Gates from a book written in the Marathi language
by Mrs. Ramabai Ranade. New York, Toronto:
Longmans Green, 1938. xiv, 253 p.

The author was the wife of Justice Mahadev Govind
Ranade, and the book is the story of her life with him;
excellent for a study of interpersonal relations in a
Maratha Brahman household in the latter part of the
nineteenth century in and around Poona and Bombay.

RANA SARMA, M. V., *The Stream (A Novel).* Masulipatam:
Triveni Publishers [1956] ii, 214 p.

The author writes in the introduction: "In this novel I
have attempted an explanation of the essential nature of
Man, Life and Universe."

RAO, Raja, *The Cow of the Barricades and Other Stories*
[London]: Oxford University Press [1947] (Champak Library) vii, 181 p.
Nine stories, one written originally in Kanada, the others in English; a couple are fantasies, others, realistic tales; except for one, Kanada is the locale.

Kanthapura. London: G. Allen and Unwin [1938] 9, 269, 13 p.
A small village in southern Bombay is caught up in the Nationalist movement in the early 1930's.

RAY, A. K., *Gobra: The Story of an Indian Life from the Memoirs of* . . . Benares: Gobardan Das Chowdhury, 1929. i, i, i, 190, 10 p.

RAY, Bani, *Srilata and Sampa, A Novel*. Calcutta: Mitra and Ghosh, 1953.

RAY, Lila, *Broken Bread, Short Stories of Modern Bengal*, Compiled, edited, translated by . . . Calcutta: M. C. Sarkar [1957] xxii, 260 p.
Twenty-one stories; authors include: Rabindranath Tagore, Sarat Chandra Chatterjee, Tarasankar Bandyopadhyay, Premendra Mitra and others.

RAY, Prafulla Chandra, *Life and Experiences of a Bengali Chemist*. Calcutta: Chukervertty, Chatterjee; London: Kegan Paul, Trench, Trübner, 1932. x, 557 p.
Part I is Autobiographical; Part II, Educational, Industrial, Economic, and Social; the whole is a very impersonal account of men and events of his time.

ROY, Banga Chandra, *The Story of My Life*. Part I. [Dacca: B. N. Sarkar, East Bengal Press, 1913] 97 p.
Born in Dacca District, 1839, the author played a

prominent part in the Brahmo Samaj movement in East Bengal; his book is almost entirely devoted to his religious activities.

ROY, Dilip Kumar, *The Upward Spiral. A Novel*. Bombay, New York, [etc.]: Jaico Publishing House [1949] 577 p.

Philosophical discourse within the framework of a novel; the author is (or was at the time) a member of the Sri Aurobindo ashram; the characters are for the most part Bengalis.

ROY, Motilal, *My Life's Partner*. Translated from Bengali by D. S. Mahalanobis. Calcutta: Prabartak Publishers [1945] 330, iv p.

Autobiographical. The story of a marriage in a middle class joint family in Calcutta; the husband is a seeker, and eventually a disciple of Sri Aurobindo; and the wife, a martyr. Period: early part of this century.

SAHGAL, Nayantara, *Prison and Chocolate Cake*. New York: Knopf, 1954. xvi, 236 p.

Nehru's niece recalls her early life at home and at school in India, and at school in the United States.

A Time to Be Happy. New York: Knopf, 1958. 277 p.

A picture of urban life in the U.P. and Calcutta as led by Westernized, upper-class Indians in the years before and after independence.

SARDA, Har Bilas, *Recollections and Reminiscences: Memoirs*. With a foreword by Professor K. V. Rangaswami Aiyangar. Ajmer: [B. S. Swarup] 1951. xiv, 172 p.

This is the man whose name has become attached to the Child Marriage Restraint Act; his recollections concern for the most part his extensive travels and the people he met during the course of his life.

Sathianadhan, Kamala, *Detective Janaki*. Bombay: Thacker, 1944. 169, 8 p.

Janaki is a South Indian girl whose vocation it is to solve mysteries; this involves her in a series of adventures.

Satthianadhan, Krupabai, *Kamala, a Story of Hindu Life* . . . With an introductory memoir by Mrs. H. B. Grigg. Madras: Srinivasa, Varadachari; Bombay: Mrs. R. A. Sagoon, 1894. xxxvii, 208 p.

In part a romantic tale with the scene laid in Nasik District in the nineteenth century; in part a realistic story of an unfortunate girl's life with her husband's family; the novel contains a good deal of ethnography.

Saguna: A Story of Native Christian Life by . . . With a Preface by Mrs. R. S. Benson. Madras: Srinivasa, Varadachari. Bombay: Mrs. Radhabai Atmaram Sagoon, 1895. xii, 247, xvii p.

The author's parents were the first Brahman converts to Christianity in Bombay Presidency. She herself was the first woman to enter Madras Medical College. This book is the story of her life until the time of her marriage; it contains much information on the Christian community in Bombay and Maharashtra in the latter half of the nineteenth century; several chapters devoted to an account of her parents' early life and conversion describe orthodox Brahman family life.

Sen, Ela, *Darkening Days, Being a Narrative of Famine-Stricken Bengal*. Calcutta: Susil Gupta, 1944. 179 p.

Seven stories, culled, according to the author, from real life, of women victims of the famine; plus a couple of statistical articles on the famine.

Sen Gupta, Naresh Chunder, *The Idiot's Wife*. Madras: G. A. Natesan (1935?)

SERVER-EL-MULK, Nawab Bahadur, *My Life: Autobiography of* . . . London: 1931.

SHARAR, Dewan, *The Gong of Shiva.* London: George G. Harrap, 1935. 7, 254 p.

SHINDE, B. G., *Modern Marathi Short Stories.* Bombay: Published by B. G. Shinde, Saroj Prakasam, n.d. Printed by T. C. Venkatesan at Jupiter Press, Madras. 127 p.
The volume contains an introduction by V. G. Gokak in which he discusses characteristics of Marathi literature. A collection of ten stories by different authors, including N. S. Phadke and B. G. Shinde; most of the stories are translations from Marathi and depict various facets of modern Indian life.

SHRINAGESH, Shakuntala, *The Little Black Box.* London: Secker and Warburg, 1955. 202 p.
A woman about to die in a North Indian sanatorium tells the story of her life.

SINGH, Gulab, *Thorns and Thistles (Autobiography of a Revolutionary).* Bombay: The National Information and Publications [1948] 274 p.
Sentenced for conspiracy, the author spent the years from 1933 to 1946 in Lahore Jail; aside from the first few chapters which describe his role in the revolutionary movement in Punjab, the book is devoted to jail experiences.

SINGH, Huthi, *Maura.* With an introduction by E. M. Forster. London: Constable, 1951. viii, 346 p.
The locale is a fictitious Rajput State; the hero, a eunuch; the time, the twentieth century.

SINGH, Sirdar Jogendra, *Kamla*. London: Selwyn and
Blount, 1925. 279 p.

Kamni. Lahore: (1932 ?)

According to Srinivasa Iyengar (p. 176) the heroine is
the daughter of a village barber who goes with her
father to seek work in the city, and after various
adventures comes into contact with a lady missionary.

Nasrin, An Indian Medley. London: James Nisbet,
1911. 311 p.

Srinivasa Iyengar (pp. 175–176) says this is a "peep
into 'high' life, the sensual and futile life of nawabs and
taluqdars who eat and drink and inhabit the sensual
Purgatory of their own creation."

Nur Jahan, The Romance of an Indian Queen. London:
James Nisbet, 1909. 260 p.

This historical novel ends with the marriage of Nur
Jahan to Jehangir; depicts life at the court of Akbar.

SINGH, Khushwant, *Mano Majra*. New York: Grove Press
[1956] 181 p. Also published under the title, *Train
to Pakistan, A Novel*, London: Chatto and Windus,
1956. 206 p.

A somewhat reportorial account of events in a Punjab
border village in 1947; some light here and there on
Punjabi value system.

The Mark of Vishnu and Other Stories. [London]: The
Saturn Press, 1950. 122 p.

Fourteen stories depicting various types of Punjabis.

The Voice of God and Other Stories. Bombay: Jaico
Publishing House.

SINGH, General Mohan, *Leaves from My Diary*. Lahore:
Free-World Publications, 1946. 91 p.

The diary was kept January–May, 1946, while author was imprisoned in the Red Fort, Delhi; this is mainly a personal record of his thoughts and feelings; but it contains some information on the INA and various political figures.

SORABJI, Cornelia, *Between the Twilights: Being Studies of Indian Women by One of Themselves*. London and New York: Harper, 1908. ix, 191 p.

These fourteen pieces add to and round out the pictures of Indian women she gives in her other books.

India Calling; The Memories of . . . London: Nisbet [1935] xv, 308 p.

The first fifty pages are devoted to a sketch of her early years, and to her recollections of England where she studied at Oxford; the major portion of the book recounts the experiences of this remarkable woman as legal adviser in cases involving purdah women, many of them in princely states or zamindari families; the book throws much light on the lives and problems of women of this class.

Love and Life Behind the Purdah. With an introductory note by the Marchioness of Dufferin and Ava and letter to the author from the Right Hon. Lord Hobhouse, K.C.S.I. London: Freemantle, 1901. xxii, 239 p.

Eleven stories, most of them portraying Indian women; the characters of one are Parsis.

Sun-Babies, Studies in the Child Life of India. London: John Murray, 1904. 148 p.

Eight sketches and stories of Indian children, one a Parsi child; some ethnography.

Subba Rao, K., *Revived Memories*. With a foreword by the Rt. Hon. V. S. Srinivasa Sastri. Madras: Ganesh [1933] xv, 518 p.

Author was for a time Sub-Editor of *The Hindu*; Joint-Editor of the *Indian Social Reformer*; Assistant Commissioner, Mysore; and Political Member, Dewas (J); he has recorded his recollections of men and events of his time.

Subba Rao, M. Chenna, *Myself and Rural Life* (*Auto-biography*) *Part I*. [Anantapur] Deena Bandhu [1951–] iv, 57, 10 p.

"This Autobiography is the Off-Spring of the truggles [sic] in rural life." (Pref.) Author is described in the introduction as a "longstanding field worker and Satyagrahi of the Congress, with some record of Khadi service in the background." He also had an ayurvedic dispensary for about twenty years.

Subba Rau, R. Venkata, ed., *Kamala's Letters to Her Husband*. Madras: English Publishing House, 1902. 223 p.

Essentially a tract on certain "social evils", e.g. child marriage, polygamy, the ban on widow-marriage.

Subrahmanyam, A., *Indira Devi: A Romance of Modern Political India*. Madras: Ganesh, 1930. iii, 267 p.

A review in the *Modern Review*, April, 1931, vol. XLIX, says this gives "an outline of the year 1951" and quotes the end: "When the Viceroy in tune steps aside from the Supreme Council, it may become the Dominion Parliament of the Princes and peoples of India."

SUNITY DEVEE, Maharani of Cooch Behar, *The Autobiography of an Indian Princess*. London: John Murray, 1921. 251 p.

Born 1864, daughter of Keshub Chander Sen; it was her marriage which split the Brahmo Samaj; to this, and events leading up to it, she devotes a couple of chapters. For the most part, she writes of her husband and children, and the members of the British royal family and aristocracy with whom she came into contact as one of the first Maharanis to lead a public life.

TAGORE, Devendranath, *The Autobiography of Maharshi*. . . Translated from the original Bengali by Satyendranath Tagore and Indira Devi. London: Macmillan, 1916. xliii, 295 p.

Mainly a record of the spiritual life and development of this famous nineteenth century mystic and religious leader; the book covers the first forty-one years of his life; valuable for its account of the Brahmo Samaj during the years 1842–1859.

TAGORE, Rabindranath, *Broken Ties and Other Stories*. London: Macmillan, 1925. 229 p.

Broken Ties is a long short story (126 p.) depicting the conflict between the orthodox and the modern, Western-educated members of the same family; also of value for its insights into Bengali Vaishnavism.

Farewell, My Friend. (Translated by K. R. Kripilani). London: New India Publishers, 1946. 80 p.

This is a translation of *Shesher Kavitā*, Last Poem, first published 1929. A love story with an unhappy ending; the chief male character is an ultra-modern Bengali whose Oxford education and Western experience prove to be his undoing.

Four Chapters. Calcutta: Visva- Bharati [1950] ix, 85 p. Translated from the Bengali *Chār Adhyāya* by Surendranath Tagore. Tagore writes in a foreword: ". . . its main interest centers around the story of two modern Bengali lovers. The revolutionary movement in Bengal has provided their love with its special dramatic setting." The period is the early part of the twentieth century.

Glimpses of Bengal, Selected from the Letters of Sir . . . 1885–1895. London: Macmillan, 1921. vii, 166, 2 p. A personal record, for the most part reflections on Nature, Man and God.

The Golden Boat. Translated by Bhabani Bhattacharya. Bombay [etc.] Jaico Publishing House, 1956. 122 p. A miscellany of short tales and sketches. This is not a translation of the Bengali *Sōnār Tārī*.

Gora. Translated into English by the Author. London: Macmillan, 1924. v, 408 p. Excellent picture of nineteenth century life in Calcutta, especially with reference to Brahmo Samajists and orthodox Hindus of the period.

The Home and the World. New York: Macmillan, 1919. viii, 293 p. A translation of the Bengali *Ghare Bāire*. J. C. Ghosh considers this and *Gora* "perhaps the best novels written by an Indian" (p. 175). The three main characters, the wife, her husband, and a leader of the Swadeshi movement, tell the story of the upheaval in a wealthy Bengal raja's family resulting from the intrusion of the *swadeshiwala*. Tagore expresses his views on the theory and methods of Bengali revolutionaries. Much information on domestic manners and customs, and interpersonal relations.

Hungry Stones, and Other Stories. Translated from the
    original Bengali by various writers. New York:
    Macmillan, 1916. 3, 271 pp.

Thirteen stories. The title story is a poetic fantasy; one,
an allegory; another, a fairy tale; most of them depict
various facets of life in Bengal in the late nineteenth
century.

Mashi and Other Stories; Translated from the original
    Bengali by various writers. New York: Macmillan,
    1918. 4, 3, 222 p.

Fourteen stories. For the ethnographer's purposes this
is one of the best collections of Tagore's stories. As a
whole they provide much information on the Bengali
way of life in the late nineteenth century, and on the
nature of interpersonal relations, attitudes and values.

My Boyhood Days. Translated from Bengali by Marjorie
    Sykes. [Santiniketan, Bengal: P. K. Mukherji,
    1928?] 54 p.

Charming recollections of boyhood; slight, but affords
some light on family life; takes Tagore up to his first
departure for England.

My Reminiscences. New York: Macmillan, 1917. ix,
    273 p.

Translated from Bengali (*Jivan-smriti*). Written about
1912 when Tagore was fifty years old, these reminiscences pertain for the most part to his first twenty years,
and contain much information on life in the Tagore joint
family as well as some material on men of letters and
literary activities of the period.

The Parrot's Training, and Other Stories. Calcutta:
    Visva-Bharati [1944] 39, v p.

Four allegorical tales in which Tagore satirizes aspects
of modern Indian life.

Two Sisters. Calcutta: Visva-Bharati [1945] 111, 3 p.
Translated by Krishna Kripalani. A study of the relationship between two sisters of contrasting character,
and the husband of one of them. Tagore states in the
opening sentence: "Women are of two kinds,—the
mother-kind and the beloved-kind . . ." It is the
mother-kind who triumphs in the end and keeps her
husband.

Stories from Tagore. New York: Macmillan, 1918. 3,
237 p.
More Stories from Tagore. Calcutta [etc.]: Macmillan,
1951. vii, 152 p.
The first volume contains ten stories; the second,
twelve. All, except two stories in the first volume,
appear in *Hungry Stones, and Other Stories, Mashi, and
Other Stories*, or *Broken Ties, and Other Stories*.

The Wreck. New York: Macmillan, 1921. 347 p.
A translation of *Naukādubi*. A romantic love story;
characters for the most part are upperclass, Westernized
Bengalis of Calcutta; heroine is a true Indian woman
with traditional virtues. As in other novels of Tagore,
this one affords much information on family life and
interpersonal relations.

TATTVABHUSAN, Sitanath, *Autobiography: With Details of
Philosophical Study and Spiritual Endeavour*. Calcutta: D. M. Bag [1942?] 127 p.

TILAK, Lakshimibai, *I Follow After, an Autobiography*.
Translated by Josephine Inkster. [Madras, New
York, India Branch] Oxford University Press [1950]
iv, 353 p.
Original is in Marathi. Author was wife of Narayan
Waman Tilak, well-known Indian Christian, poet and

writer of hymns, who became converted after his marriage. His wife eventually "follows after." Her autobiography contains much information on life in the latter part of the nineteenth century among Maratha Brahmans as well as material on Indian Christians at this period.

VENKATARAMANI, K. S., *A Day with Sambhu*. Madras: Svetaranya Ashrama [1929] 63 p.
Moral lessons imparted by a sadhu to a small boy; in form, a kind of prose poem.

Jatadharan and Other Stories. Madras: Svetaranya Ashrama [1937] viii, 156 p.
Nine sketches and short stories; one is a historical tale in the time of Tipu Sultan; the others describe various types and incidents in present-day South India.

Kandan, the Patriot. Madras: Svetaranya Ashrama [1934] 288 p.
Plot is concerned with incidents in the Swarajist movement about 1930 in and around Tranquebar, in South India; events culminate in a riot; the characters give expression to the ideals of the movement.

Murugan, the Tiller. London: Simpkin, Marshall, Hamilton, Kent, 1927. viii, 309 p.
In spite of the title this is not strictly speaking a novel of peasant life; the main characters are a government servant, a city lawyer, and Murugan, whose lives are intertwined.

Paper Boats. Madras: Theosophical Publishing House, 1921. xii, 121 p.
Ten sketches—the Indian Beggar, the Hindu Temple, The Hindu Pilgrim, My Grandmother, and similar subjects.

VENKATESA IYENGAR, Masti, *Short Stories, in Four Volumes*. With a Foreword by Sri C. Rajagopalachar. [Cottonpet, Bangalore City: Printed at the B. B. D. Power Press] 1943. ix, 184; 194; 191; 194 p.

Each volume contains eight stories dealing for the most part with Kannada village life, and useful for their ethnographic detail; all but one of the stories in the fourth volume are imaginary tales of legendary or historical persons.

Subbanna (A Story).

VENUGOPAL, T., *Parvati*. Bezwada.

According to a review in the *Modern Review*, Vol. LV, June, 1934, p. 694, this is "A story of post-puberty marriage . . . social evils are admirably dealt with . . ."

VENUGOPAL, T. K., *Tales of Kerala*. Tripunittura: Lakshmi Variety Stories, 1119 [1943–44] 46 p.

VIDYABINOD, Kedarnath Chakravarti, *The Liberation: A High-Class Devotional Novel, Ethical and Philanthropical*. Calcutta: Bejay Gopal Chakravarti, 1924, viii, 270, xxii p.

VITTAL RAO, Ananda, *Glamour, and Other Stories*. Bangalore: B. B. D. Power Press, 1950. 80 p.

The Man in the Red Tie, and Other Stories. Bombay: International Book House, 1942. 167 p.

The first of these volumes contains ten stories; the second, fifteen; they depict various aspects of Indian life; the characters are, for the most part, educated, upperclass townsmen.

YOGANANDA, Paramhansa, *Autobiography of a Yogi*. With a preface by W. Y. Evans-Wentz. New York: The Philosophical Library [1946] xvi, 498 p.

Yogananda, a Bengali, (Mukunda Lal Ghosh), was born in the last decade of the nineteenth century, came to the United States in 1920 as Indian delegate to the International Congress of Religious Liberals, and eventually founded a Yoga Institute in California. His book deals largely with his religious training and activities in India and with the holy men with whom he was associated.